CARNEGIE LEARNING MATH SERIES COURSE 2

STUDENT EDITION
VOLUME 2
4TH EDITION

SANDY BARTLE FINOCCHI

WILLIAM S. HADLEY

MARY LOU METZ

MARY LYNN RAITH

JANET SINOPOLI

JACLYN SNYDER

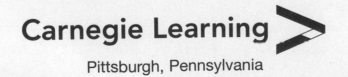

Pittsburgh, Pennsylvania

Carnegie Learning >

437 Grant St., Suite 1906
Pittsburgh, PA 15219
Phone 888.851.7094
Customer Service Phone 888.851.7094, option 3

www.carnegielearning.com

Printing History
First Edition 2011
Second Edition 2014
Third Edition 2015
Fourth Edition 2016

ISBN: 978-1-60972-591-4
Set ISBN: 978-1-60972-111-4

Printed in the United States of America by Cenveo Corporation
1 2 3 4 5 6 7 8 9 CC 18 17 16

Dear Student,

You are about to begin an exciting journey! These mathematical materials were written specifically for *you*, a middle school student. The book you are holding is *your* book. There is lots of space for writing, sketching, drawing, cutting, pasting, and constructing new mathematical ideas. You may want to highlight key terms, take notes in the margins, or even doodle on the cover.

Connections are important in life. The popularity of social networks shows the importance of connections. In much the same way, mathematics connects with so many activities in our lives. Throughout the lessons, you will build new knowledge based upon your prior knowledge. You will apply math to real-world situations so that you can see why it's meaningful. You will encounter models that portray mathematical concepts. Models will be presented in all sorts of ways—from lesson openers, to pictures, to different student methods and approaches to problem solving. You will also use manipulatives, which are objects that you can use to model or reinforce key mathematical concepts.

Of course, if you need additional practice, you can find it in your Assignments and Skills Practice book. Keep in mind, no professional athlete practices by just playing an entire game—ballet dancers repeat some basic steps, moves, and dances; basketball players practice dribbling, shooting, and defending; even writers jot ideas for novels in their spare time—all to improve their skills. Mathematics is no different and these materials enable and encourage you to practice.

Don't worry—you will not be working alone. We encourage students to work together in pairs or in groups because it gets you talking about your insights. Everyone will share his or her ideas and thoughts in class. Sometimes you will help your classmates, and other times they will help you.

Today's workplace demands teamwork and self-confidence. At Carnegie Learning, we have designed a Math Series to help you to make the most of your math course. Enjoy the journey and share your thoughts with others. Have fun while Learning by Doing!

The Carnegie Learning® Curriculum Development Team

ACKNOWLEDGMENTS

Carnegie Learning Curriculum Development Team

- David Dengler
  Director, Curriculum Development

- Jen Gansberger
  Editorial Assistant

- Lezlee Ross
  Curriculum Developer

- Joshua Fisher
  Math Editor

- David "Augie" Rivera
  Math Editor

Advisory Board

- Shelly Allen, Richmond County Schools
- Ryan Baker, Worcester Polytechnic Institute
- Bill Bush, University of Louisville
- John McCook, McCook and Associates
- Roxana Moreno, University of New Mexico
- Doug Rohrer, University of South Florida
- Bob Siegler, Carnegie Mellon University
- Mary Ann Stine, Private Consultant

Vendors

- Bookmasters, Inc.
- Mathematical Expressions
- ESI Design
- Cenveo Corporation

Special Thanks

- Content contributors: Janet Falkowski, Ken Labuskes, Marianne O'Connor, Jennifer Panasko, Agnes Pavolovich
- Peter Arkle for the design and rendering of "The Crew"
- Richmond County School District, Georgia, for piloting lessons and providing implementation feedback
- Carnegie Learning Managers of School Partnership for content and design review
- The Children of Carnegie Learning employees for providing a "middle-schooler's" perspective, with special recognition to:
  - Matthew B.
  - Dawson D.
  - Allison M.
  - Adam, Nic, and Shane R.
  - Aaron and Melinda R.

Photograph Credits

Chapter 1 © istockphoto.com/gaffera;

Chapter 2 © istockphoto.com/Amanda Rohde;

Chapter 3 © istockphoto.com/Nathan Maxfield;

Chapter 4 © istockphoto.com/Michael Flippo;

Chapter 5 © istockphoto.com/Pgiam;

Chapter 6 © istockphoto.com/Pavels Sabelnikovs;

Chapter 7 © istockphoto.com/Michael Smith;

Chapter 8 © istockphoto.com/Peter Andersen;

Chapter 9 © istockphoto.com/Richard Hobson;

Chapter 10 © istockphoto.com/Gary Blakeley;

Chapter 11 © istockphoto.com/Daniel Cooper;

Chapter 12 © istockphoto.com/Joze Pojbic;

Chapter 13 © istockphoto.com/sandramo;

Chapter 14 © istockphoto.com/Mark Rose;

Chapter 15 © istockphoto.com/Sam Kittner/Courtesy Newseum;

Chapter 16 © istockphoto.com/Patrick Heagny;

Chapter 17 © istockphoto.com/Suzanne Tucker

TABLE OF CONTENTS

Table of Contents

Table of Contents

Table of Contents

Table of Contents

PROBABILITY OF COMPOUND EVENTS_____90

Table of Contents

Table of Contents

THE CREW

The Crew is here to help you on your journey. Sometimes they will remind you about things you already learned. Sometimes they will ask you questions to help you think abo[ut] different strategies. Sometimes they will share fun facts. They are members of your group—someone you can rely on!

Teacher aides will guide you along your journey. They will help you make connections and remind you to think about the details.

MATHEMATICAL REPRESENTATIONS

Introduction

During this course, you will solve problems and work with many different representations of mathematical concepts, ideas, and processes to better understand the world. Each lesson will provide you with opportunities to discuss your ideas, work within groups, and share your solutions and methods with your class. These process icons are placed throughout the text.

Discuss to Understand

- Read the problem carefully.
- What is the context of the problem? Do we understand it?
- What is the question that we are being asked? Does it make sense?
- Is this problem similar to some other problem we know?

Think for Yourself

- Do I need any additional information to answer the question?
- Is this problem similar to some other problem that I know?
- How can I represent the problem using a picture, a diagram, symbols, or some other representation?

Work with Your Partner

- How did you do the problem?
- Show me your representation.
- This is the way I thought about the problem—how did you think about it?
- What else do we need to solve the problem?
- Does our reasoning and our answer make sense to each other?
- How will we explain our solution to the class?

Share with the Class

- Here is our solution and the methods we used.
- Are we communicating our strategies clearly?
- We could only get this far with our solution. How can we finish?
- Could we have used a different strategy to solve the problem?

ACADEMIC GLOSSARY

Key Terms of the Course

There are important terms you will encounter throughout this book. It is important that yc
have an understanding of these words as you get started on your journey through the
mathematical concepts. Knowing what is meant by these terms and using these terms w
help you think, reason, and communicate your ideas. The Graphic Organizers shown
display a definition for a key term, related words, sample questions, and examples.

You will create graphic organizers like these as your own references of key math ideas.

My folks are always trying to get me to be organized!

DEFINITION

To study or look closely for patterns. Analyzing can involve examining or breaking a concept down into smaller parts to gain a better understanding of it.

RELATED WORDS

- examine
- evaluate
- determine
- observe
- consider
- investigate
- what do you notice?
- what do you think?
- sort and match

ASK YOURSELF

- Do I see any patterns?
- Have I seen something like this before?
- What happens if the shape, representation, or numbers change?

ANALYZE

EXAMPLE

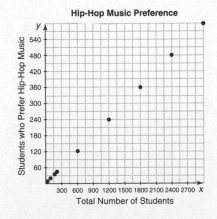

Hip-Hop Music Preference

4. Examine each graph and describe the pattern of the points.

The points all increase as the total number of students increase. The points seem to be in a straight line.

DEFINITION

To give details or describe how to determine an answer or solution.
Explaining your reasoning helps justify conclusions.

RELATED WORDS

- show your work
- explain your calculation
- justify
- why or why not?

ASK YOURSELF

- How should I organize my thoughts?
- Is my explanation logical?
- Does my reasoning make sense?
- How can I justify my answer to others?

Don't forget to check your answers!

EXPLAIN YOUR REASONING

EXAMPLE

In order to build a balsa wood model of the Wright brothers' plane, you would need to cut long lengths of wood spindles into shorter lengths for the wing stays, the vertical poles that support and connect the two wings. Each stay for the main wings of the model needs to be cut $3\frac{1}{4}$ inches long.

Show your work and explain your reasoning.

1. If the wood spindles are each 10 inches long, how many stays could you cut from one spindle?

$$10 \div 3\frac{1}{4} = \frac{10}{1} \times \frac{4}{13}$$
$$= \frac{40}{13}$$
$$= 3\frac{1}{13}$$

I could cut three stays because 10 divided by $3\frac{1}{4}$ is $3\frac{1}{13}$, so there are 3 full pieces and $\frac{1}{13}$ of a stay left over.

DEFINITION

To display information in various ways. Representing mathematics can be done using words, tables, graphs, or symbols.

RELATED WORDS

- show
- sketch
- draw
- create
- plot
- graph
- write an equation
- complete the table

ASK YOURSELF

- How should I organize my thoughts?
- How do I use this model to show a concept or idea?
- What does this representation tell me?
- Is my representation accurate?

REPRESENT

EXAMPLE

4. During the summer, Matthew and Devan started their own business mowing lawns for people in the Lake Section. Before starting any work, Matthew spent $15 to fill up the gas tank for the lawnmower. The boys agreed that each person would earn the same amount after Matthew was reimbursed the money he spent for gas. After a week of work, the boys were paid a total of $243. Matthew filled up the gas tank just once. How much did each boy earn?

a. Draw a picture to represent the situation. Label the unknown parts with variables and the known parts with their values.

DEFINITION

To make an educated guess based on the analysis of given data.
Estimating first helps inform reasoning.

RELATED WORDS

- predict
- approximate
- expect
- about how much?

ASK YOURSELF

- Does my reasoning make sense?
- Is my solution close to my estimation?

Estimating gets you in the neighborhood, calculating gets you the address.

ESTIMATE

EXAMPLE

Most restaurant patrons add a tip to the final bill to show their appreciation for their wait staff. Usually, a patron will determine 15% or 20% of the bill, and then add that amount to the total. Many times, patrons will just round off the tip to the nearest dollar. For patrons tipping 20%, determining the amount of a tip is easier. Twenty percent is one-fifth, so to determine the tip, patrons only need to divide the rounded bill by 5.

For example, if the bill is $38.95, you would round to 40, and then divide by 5. The 20% tip should be about $8.

1. Estimate a 20% tip for each of the bills shown.
   a. $89.45
      This is about $90. So, a reasonable tip will be about $90 divided by 5, which is $18.

DEFINITION

To represent or give an account of in words. Describing communicates mathematical ideas to others.

RELATED WORDS

- demonstrate
- label
- display
- compare
- define
- determine
- what are the advantages?
- what are the disadvantages?
- what is similar?
- what is different?

ASK YOURSELF

- How should I organize my thoughts?
- Is my explanation logical?
- Did I consider the context of the situation?
- Does my reasoning make sense?

DESCRIBE

EXAMPLE

1. The amount a contractor gets paid (p) is directly proportional to the number of days worked (d).

   a. Complete the table of values.

d	p (dollars)
0	0
1	250
2	500
3.5	875

   b. Determine the constant of proportionality and describe what it represents in this problem situation.

   The constant of proportionality, or k, is 250. The contractor makes $250 for every day he or she works.

Problem Types You Will See

Worked Example

A number line can be used to model integer addition.

When adding a positive integer, move to the right on a number line.

When adding a negative integer, move to the left on a number line.

Example 1: The number line shows how to determine $5 + 8$.

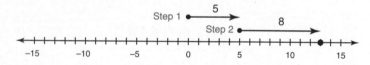

Example 2: The number line shows how to determine $5 + (-8)$.

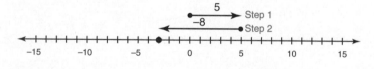

2. Compare the first steps in each example.

a. What distance is shown by the first term in each example?

   The distance shown by the first term in each example is the same: 5 units.

b. Describe the graphical representation of the first term. Where does it start and in which direction does it move? Why?

   The graphical representation for the first term begins at 0 and moves to the right. It moves to the right because the first term is positive.

c. What is the absolute value of the first term in each example?

   The absolute value of 5 is 5.

Katie used Corinne's method to solve this problem:

1. Explain why Katie's answer is incorrect. Then, determine the correct answer.

The $46 was the discount, not what Katie paid for the flight. Katie must subtract the discount:
$229.99 - $46 = $183.99.

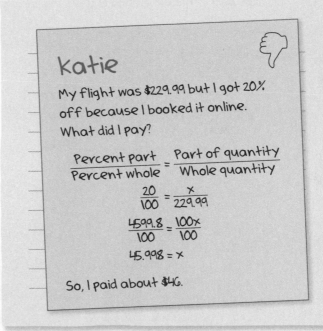

Katie

My flight was $229.99 but I got 20% off because I booked it online. What did I pay?

$$\frac{\text{Percent part}}{\text{Percent whole}} = \frac{\text{Part of quantity}}{\text{Whole quantity}}$$

$$\frac{20}{100} = \frac{x}{229.99}$$

$$\frac{4599.8}{100} = \frac{100x}{100}$$

$$45.998 = x$$

So, I paid about $46.

Thumbs Up

Vicki also used Corinne's method but, got the answer without having to subtract:

2. Explain why Vicki's method worked.

Twenty percent off is the same as 80% of something.

If I take 40% off $100, that's $100 – $40. That leaves me with $60, which is 100% – 40%, or 60%. Hmmmm . . .

Vicki

My flight was $229.99 but I got 20% off because I booked it online. What did I pay?

$$\frac{\text{Percent part}}{\text{Percent whole}} = \frac{\text{Part of quantity}}{\text{Whole quantity}}$$

$$\frac{80}{100} = \frac{x}{229.99}$$

$$\frac{18399.2}{100} = \frac{100x}{100}$$

$$183.99 = x$$

Problem Types

▶ Take your time to read through the situation.

▶ Question the strategy or reason given.

▶ Determine correct or not correct.

▶ Does the reasoning make sense?

▶ If the reasoning makes sense, what is the justification?

▶ If the reasoning does not make sense, what error was made?

Examine the spinner shown.

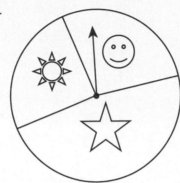

1. Jonah makes the follow predictions for the spinner landing on each symbol. Do you think his predictions are correct?

$$P(\text{☺}) = \frac{1}{4} \qquad P(\text{☀}) = \frac{1}{4} \qquad P(\text{★}) = \frac{2}{5}$$

Jonah's predictions are incorrect because the sum of the probabilities of the three outcomes is not equal to 1.

Problem Types

9 USING GEOMETRY

9

Recognize these tools? The one on the right is a protractor, which has been used since ancient times to measure angles. The one on the left is a compass, used to create arcs and circles. You can even use the bottom of the protractor as a straightedge—two tools in one!

9.1 EARTH MEASURE
Introduction to Geometry and Geometric Constructions

Learning Goals

In this lesson, you will:

▶ Sketch and draw figures.

▶ Use a compass to construct circles.

▶ Use geometric tools to duplicate line segments.

Key Terms

▶ geometry
▶ protractor
▶ compass
▶ straightedge
▶ sketch
▶ draw
▶ construct

▶ geometric construction
▶ point
▶ line
▶ plane
▶ coplanar lines
▶ skew lines

▶ line segment
▶ endpoints
▶ arc
▶ congruent line segments
▶ congruent
▶ intersection

In this unit, you will be studying the field of mathematics called *geometry*. **Geometry** is the study of shapes and measurement. The word "geometry" comes from the Greek prefix "geo," which means "earth," and the Greek word "metria," which means "measure." So, the original meaning of "geometry" is "to measure the earth."

Geometry is one of the oldest fields in mathematics. The Egyptians used geometry to build their pyramids, the Greeks to build their Parthenon, the Mayans to build their temples, and Americans to build our skyscrapers. Where else have you encountered geometry? What are other examples of famous structures that people built using geometry?

Problem 1 Creating Figures Using Writing and Geometry Tools

Producing pictures, sketches, diagrams, and drawings of figures is a very important part of geometry. Many tools can be used to create geometric figures. Some tools, such as a ruler or a protractor, are classified as measuring tools. A **protractor** can be used to approximate the measure of an angle. A **compass** is a tool used to create arcs and circles. A **straightedge** is a ruler with no numbers. It is important to know when to use each tool.

- When you **sketch** a geometric figure, the figure is created without the use of tools.

- When you **draw** a geometric figure, the figure is created with the use of tools such as a ruler, a straightedge, a compass, or a protractor. A drawing is generally more accurate than a sketch.

- When you **construct** a geometric figure, the figure is created using only a compass and a straightedge. A construction can also be called a **geometric construction**.

Look at the figure shown.

1. Make a sketch of the figure.

2. Make a drawing of the figure.

3. Compare your sketches to the sketches of the other students in your group. What do you notice about your sketch and your classmates' sketches?

Sloppy, Ugly.

4. Compare your drawings to the drawings of the other students in your group. What do you notice about your drawing and your classmates' drawings?

5. Describe what you did differently to answer Questions 1 and 2.

for 1. I rushed

6. Were the sketches or drawings more exact copies of the figure shown? Explain your reasoning.

7. Did your sketch or drawing take more time to do? Explain your reasoning.

Drawing. We used a straigt Edge

Problem 2 Building Blocks of Geometry

Three essential building blocks of geometry are point, line, and plane.

A **point** is described as a location in space. A point has no size or shape, but it is often represented using a dot and is named with a capital letter.

As examples, points *A* and *B* are shown.

A● ●*B*

A **line** is described as a straight continuous arrangement of an infinite number of points. A line has an infinite length, but no width. Arrowheads are used to indicate that a line extends infinitely in opposite directions. The line symbol is ⟵⟶.

Lines are named with either a lowercase single letter or by using two points through which the line passes with a line symbol above them. The names of the lines shown are line *m* and $\overleftrightarrow{CD}$ and are read as "line *m*" and "line *CD*."

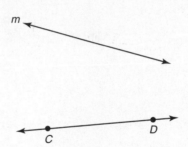

A **plane** is described as a flat surface. A plane has an infinite length and width, but no depth. A plane extends infinitely in all directions. Planes are determined by three points, but they are usually named using one lowercase letter. As an example, plane *s* is shown.

Sometimes, lines can be located in one plane. Other times, lines can be located in two different planes.

Coplanar lines are two or more lines that are located in the same plane. **Skew lines**, or non-coplanar lines, are lines that are not located in the same plane.

1. Draw and label three coplanar lines.

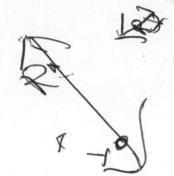

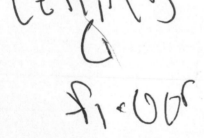

2. Look around your classroom. Describe the location of two skew lines.

ceiling

floor

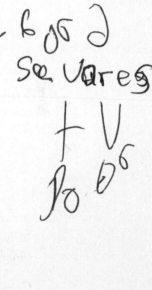

whiteboard
squares

TV
Door

Number line
floor

A **line segment** is a portion of a line that includes two points and all the points between those two points. The **endpoints** of a line segment are the points where the line segment ends. A line segment is named using the two capital letters that name its endpoints.

For example, the name of line segment *AB* can be written using symbols as $\overline{AB}$. This is read as "line segment *AB*." You should know that $\overline{AB}$ is the same as $\overline{BA}$. It does not matter which endpoint you use first to name a line segment.

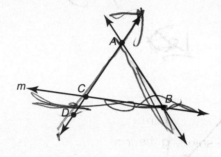

3. Use the figure shown to answer each.

    a. List all the named points.

    b. List the names of all the lines shown using symbols.

    c. List the names of all the labeled line segments in this figure using symbols.

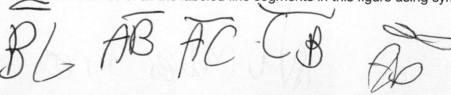

Problem 3 Fun with Circles

Remember that a compass is an instrument used to draw circles and *arcs*. A compass can have two legs connected at one end.

One leg has a point, and the other holds a pencil. Some newer compasses may be different, but all of them are made to construct circles by placing the point firmly into the paper and then spinning the top of the compass around, with the pencil point just touching the paper.

1. Use your compass to construct a number of circles of different sizes.

Take your time. It may take a while for you to be able to construct a clean, exact circle without doubled or smudged lines.

2. Construct a circle using line segment *CD* as the radius and *C* as the center.

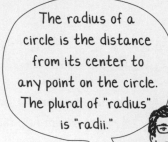

The radius of a circle is the distance from its center to any point on the circle. The plural of "radius" is "radii."

a. Draw and label points *A, B, E,* and *F* on the circle.

b. Construct $\overline{AC}$, $\overline{BC}$, $\overline{EC}$, and $\overline{FC}$.

c. What conclusion can you make about all these line segments? Explain your reasoning.

d. Do you think the line segments you constructed are also radii of the circle? How do you know?

An **arc** is a part of a circle. You can also think of an arc as the curve between two points on the circle.

3. Construct an arc using $\overline{AC}$ as the radius and *C* as the center of the circle. Make your arc about one-half inch long, and make sure that it does not pass through *A*.

a. Place and label two points *B* and *E* on the arc and construct line segments *CE* and *CB*.

b. What conclusion can you make about all these line segments?

Line segments that have the same length are called **congruent line segments.**
Congruent means to have the same size, shape, and measure. You can indicate that two line segments are congruent by using the congruence symbol, ≅ and writing the names of the line segments that are congruent on either side of it. For example, $\overline{CB} \cong \overline{CA}$ is read as "line segment *CB* is congruent to line segment *CA*."

4. Construct a circle with the center *A* and a radius of about 1 inch.

   a. Without changing the width of your compass, place the compass point on any point on the circle you constructed and then construct another circle.

   b. Place the compass point on a point of *intersection* of the two circles, and then construct another circle. An **intersection** is the point at which two or more lines or arcs intersect, or cross.

   c. Repeat this process until no new circles can be constructed.

   d. Connect the points of the circles' intersections with each other.

•*A*

   e. What figure do the line segments form?

Problem 4 Duplicate Line Segments

You can duplicate a line segment by constructing an exact copy of the original line segment.

A ● ──────── ● B

A ● ──────── ● B

A ●──●B

←────── ●──────→
C

←────── ●──────→
C

←──── ● ─● ──→
C   D

Draw a Starter Line

Use a straightedge to draw a starter line longer than segment *AB*. Label point *C* on the new segment.

Measure Length

Set your compass at the length *AB*.

Copy Length

Place the compass at *C*. Mark point *D* on the new segment.

1. Construct a line segment that is twice the length of line segment *AB*.

2. Duplicate each line segment using a compass and a straightedge.

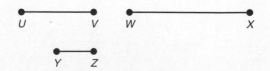

U ──── V   W ──────────── X

Y ── Z

> Make sure to draw a starter line first.

Be prepared to share your solutions and methods.

9.2 ANGLES AND MORE ANGLES

Measuring and Constructing Angles

Learning Goals

In this lesson, you will:

▶ Measure and construct angles.

▶ Duplicate angles.

▶ Bisect angles.

▶ Review congruent figures.

Key Terms

▶ ray
▶ angle
▶ sides of an angle
▶ vertex
▶ degrees (°)
▶ acute angle

▶ right angle
▶ obtuse angle
▶ straight angle
▶ congruent angles
▶ bisect
▶ angle bisector

What's the steepest angle that a roller coaster can have? You might think that the angle can't measure more than a right angle—90 degrees. But a few roller coasters in the world have "steeper" angles. One such roller coaster, called Rage, at Adventure Island in Essex County, England, has an amazing drop of 97 degrees!

But, wait. Wouldn't a 97-degree drop be *less* scary than a 90-degree drop?

Problem 1   More Building Blocks

A **ray** is a portion of a line that begins at a point and extends infinitely in one direction. Rays are named using two points. The first point represents the starting point, and the second point is any other point on the ray.

For example, the name of ray AB can be written using symbols as $\overrightarrow{AB}$, which is read as "ray AB."

1. Use $\overleftrightarrow{CD}$ to sketch each.

   a. Above $\overleftrightarrow{CD}$, sketch and label $\overrightarrow{CD}$.

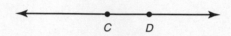

   b. Below $\overleftrightarrow{CD}$, sketch and label $\overrightarrow{DC}$.

2. Do you think it is important which letter is first when describing a ray? Explain your reasoning.

3. List all the rays labeled in the figure shown.

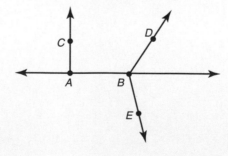

An **angle** is formed by two rays that share a common endpoint. The angle symbol is ∠. The **sides of an angle** are the two rays. The **vertex** of an angle is the common endpoint the two rays share.

Angles can be named in many ways, such as:

- by the vertex when there is only one angle with that vertex;
- a number inside the angle; and
- using three points in order: first, a point from one ray, then the vertex, and then a point from the second ray.

For example, the angle shown can be named angle B, $\angle B$, $\angle 1$, $\angle ABC$, or $\angle CBA$.

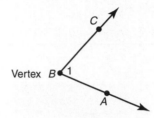

4. List all the different angles shown in the figure.

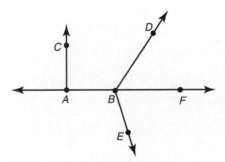

Remember that a protractor is a measuring device that can be used to approximate the measure of an angle. One unit of measure for angles is **degrees** (°).

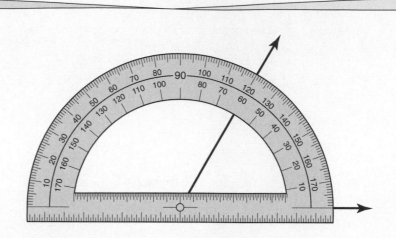

To measure an angle using a protractor:

- Align the bottom of the protractor with one side of the angle.
- Align the center of the protractor on the vertex of the angle.
- Find where the second side of the angle aligns with the angle's degree measure on the protractor.
- The measure of the angle shown is 60°.

1. What is the measure of the angle shown?

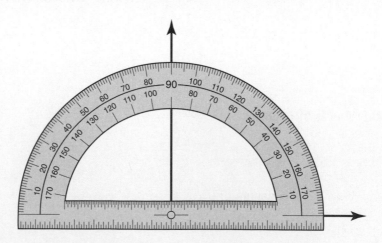

2. Is the measure of the angle shown 130° or 50°? Explain your reasoning.

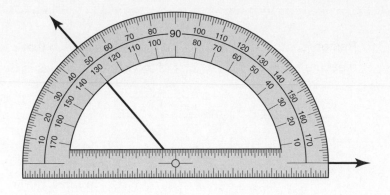

3. How do you know when to use each of the two scales on a protractor?

4. Use the diagram shown to answer each question.

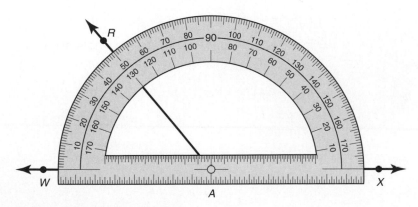

a. What is the measure of ∠*WAR*?

b. What is the measure of ∠*RAX*?

c. What is the measure of ∠*WAX*?

5. Use the diagram shown to determine the measure of each angle.

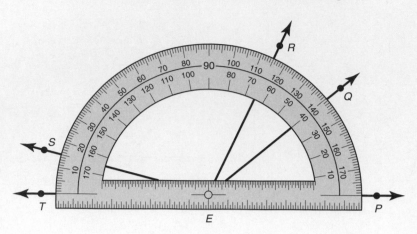

a. ∠SET

b. ∠QEP

c. ∠REQ

d. ∠REP

e. ∠TEQ

f. ∠PES

g. ∠SER

6. Use a protractor to determine the measure of each angle to the nearest degree.

a.

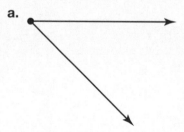

b.

7. Which angle measure is greater? Explain your reasoning.

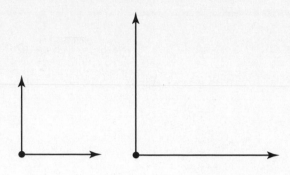

8. Use a protractor to draw an angle with the given measure.

    a. 30° angle   **b.** 130° angle

Problem 3   Classifying Angles

An **acute angle** is an angle whose measure is greater than 0° but less than 90°.

1. Draw and label an acute angle.

A **right angle** is an angle whose measure is equal to 90°. A square drawn at the vertex of the angle is used to indicate a right angle in geometric figures.

2. Draw and label a right angle.

If you don't see the right angle symbol in a diagram, don't assume it is 90°.

An **obtuse angle** is an angle whose measure is greater than 90° but less than 180°.

3. Draw and label an obtuse angle.

A **straight angle** is an angle whose measure is equal to 180°. The sides of a straight angle form a line.

4. Draw and label a straight angle.

Congruent angles are two or more angles that have equal measures. To show that two angles, such as A and B, are congruent, you can write $\angle A \cong \angle B$, which is read as "angle A is congruent to angle B."

5. Draw and label $\angle A$ and $\angle B$ such that $\angle A \cong \angle B$.

6. Use a protractor to measure $\angle A$ and $\angle B$. Then complete each statement.

    a. $m\angle A =$ _____° is read as "the measure of angle A is equal to _____ degrees."

    b. $m\angle B =$ _____° is read as "the measure of angle B is equal to _____ degrees."

    c. How do you read $m\angle DEF = 110°$?

If $m\angle A = m\angle B$, then $\angle A$ is congruent to $\angle B$ by the definition of congruent angles.

As with line segments, use the congruent symbol, $\cong$, between the angle names and the equals sign, $=$, between references to measures of angles.

Markers are used to indicate congruent angles in geometric figures. The diagram shows $\angle A \cong \angle B$.

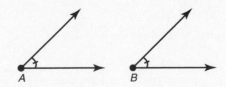

Problem 4 Duplicate Angles

You can duplicate an angle by constructing an exact copy of the original using your tools of geometry.

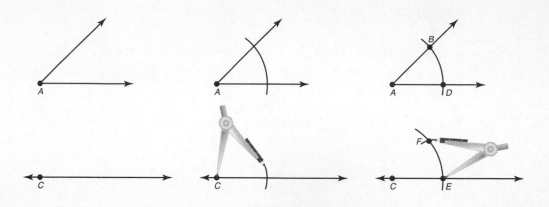

Draw a Starter Line

Use a straightedge to draw a starter line. Label point *C* on the new line.

Draw an Arc

Draw an arc with center *A* that intersects both sides of the angle. Using the same radius, draw an arc with center *C*.

Draw an Arc

Label points *B*, *D*, and *E*. Draw an arc with radius *BD* at center *E*. Label the intersection *F*.

Draw a Ray

Draw ray *CF*.
∠*BAD* ≅ ∠*FCE*.

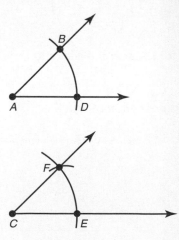

1. How wide do you set your compass to start the construction? What is important about the first arc you draw?

2. In the second step, what does "using the same radius" tell you about how to use your compass throughout the construction?

3. Construct an angle that is twice the measure of ∠A.

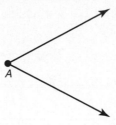

A

Problem 5 Angle Bisectors

To **bisect** means to divide into two equal parts.

1. If a line segment is bisected, what does that mean?

2. If an angle is bisected, what does that mean?

If a ray is drawn through the vertex of an angle and divides the angle into two angles of equal measure, or two congruent angles, the ray is called an **angle bisector.**

You can use tools to construct an angle bisector.

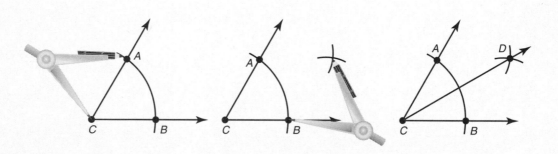

Draw an Arc

Place the compass at C. Draw an arc that intersects both sides of the angle. Label the intersections A and B.

Draw an Arc

Place the compass at A. Draw an arc, then place the compass at B. Using the same radius, draw another arc that intersects the first one.

Draw a Ray

Label the intersection of the two arcs D. Use a straightedge to draw a ray through C and D. Ray CD bisects ∠C.

3. Construct the bisector of ∠A.

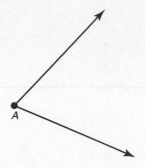

So, I set my compass once, draw three arcs, and draw a line.

A

4. Construct an angle that is one-fourth the measure of ∠H.

H

5. Describe how to construct an angle that is one-eighth the measure of angle H.

Be prepared to share your solutions and methods.

9

SPECIAL ANGLES
9.3
Complements, Supplements, Midpoints, Perpendiculars, and Perpendicular Bisectors

Learning Goals

In this lesson, you will:

▶ Calculate the supplement of an angle.
▶ Calculate the complement of an angle.
▶ Construct a perpendicular line.
▶ Construct a perpendicular bisector.
▶ Construct the midpoint of a segment.
▶ Classify adjacent angles, linear pairs, and vertical angles.

Key Terms

▶ supplementary angles
▶ complementary angles
▶ perpendicular
▶ midpoint of a segment
▶ segment bisector
▶ perpendicular bisector
▶ adjacent angles
▶ linear pair
▶ vertical angles

9

Look all around you. You can probably see right angles (square corners) and straight angles (straight lines). A famous American architect named Frank Lloyd Wright challenged these patterns with his design of the Hanna House, also known as the Honeycomb House. Wright designed the house so that none of its walls would be at right angles to each other. Instead, he used 120-degree angles. What examples of right angles and straight angles can you find around you?

Problem 1   Supplements and Complements

Two angles are **supplementary angles** if the sum of their angle measures is equal to 180

1. Use a protractor to draw a pair of supplementary angles that share a side. Then, measure each angle.

Remember "to draw" means to use your tools. . . so, get out your protractor and straightedge.

2. Use a protractor to draw a pair of supplementary angles that do not share a side. Then, measure each angle.

3. Calculate the measure of an angle that is supplementary to ∠*KJL*.

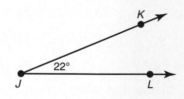

Two angles are **complementary angles** if the sum of their angle measures is equal to 90°

4. Use a protractor to draw a pair of complementary angles that share a side. Then, measure each angle.

5. Use a protractor to draw a pair of complementary angles that do not share a side. Then, measure each angle.

6. Calculate the measure of an angle that is complementary to ∠J.

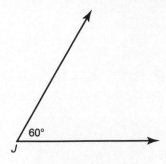

7. Two angles are both congruent and supplementary. What is the measure of each angle? Show your work, and explain your reasoning.

8. Two angles are both congruent and complementary. What is the measure of each angle? Show your work and explain your reasoning.

Problem 2   Perpendicular Relationships

Two lines, line segments, or rays are **perpendicular** if they intersect to form 90° angles. The symbol for perpendicular is ⊥.

1. Draw $\overleftrightarrow{AB} \perp \overleftrightarrow{CD}$ at point E. How many right angles are formed?

2. Draw $\overleftrightarrow{BC} \perp \overleftrightarrow{AB}$ at point B. How many right angles are formed?

3. Name all angles that you know are right angles in the figure shown.

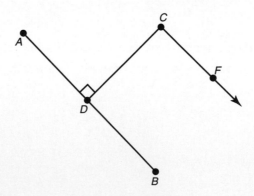

You can use tools to construct a perpendicular line through a point on another line.

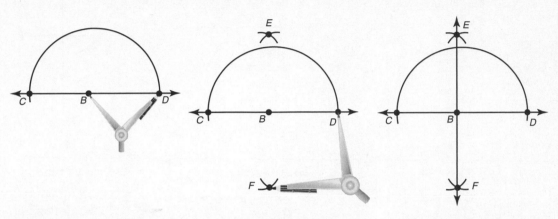

Draw an Arc

Use *B* as the center and draw an arc that intersects the line at two points. Label the intersection points *C* and *D*.

Draw Arcs

Open the compass radius. Use *C* and *D* as centers and draw intersecting arcs above and below the line. Label the intersection points *E* and *F*.

Draw a Line

Use a straightedge to connect points *E* and *F*. Line *EF* is perpendicular to line *CD*.

1. Construct a line perpendicular to the given line through point *P*.

> Why do you open the compass radius in Step 2?

You can also use tools to construct a perpendicular line through a point not on the line.

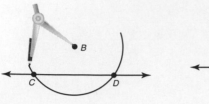 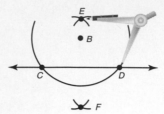 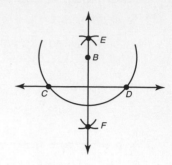

Draw an Arc

Use *B* as the center and draw an arc that intersects the line at two points. Label the intersections points *C* and *D*.

Draw Arcs

Open the compass radius. Use *C* and *D* as centers and draw intersecting arcs above and below the line. Label the intersections points *E* and *F*.

Draw a Line

Use a straightedge to connect points *E* and *F*. Line *EF* is perpendicular to line *CD*.

2. Construct a line perpendicular to $\overleftrightarrow{AG}$ through point *B*.

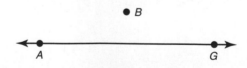

● *B*

A   G

3. How is the construction of a perpendicular through a point on the line different from the construction of a perpendicular through a point not on the line?

Problem 4 Midpoint and a Perpendicular Bisector

The **midpoint of a segment** is a point that divides the segment into two congruent segments, or two segments of equal length.

$\overline{PQ}$ has midpoint M.

A **segment bisector** is a line, line segment, or ray that divides the line segment into two line segments of equal measure, or two congruent line segments.

A **perpendicular bisector** is a line, line segment, or ray that intersects the midpoint of a line segment at a 90-degree angle.

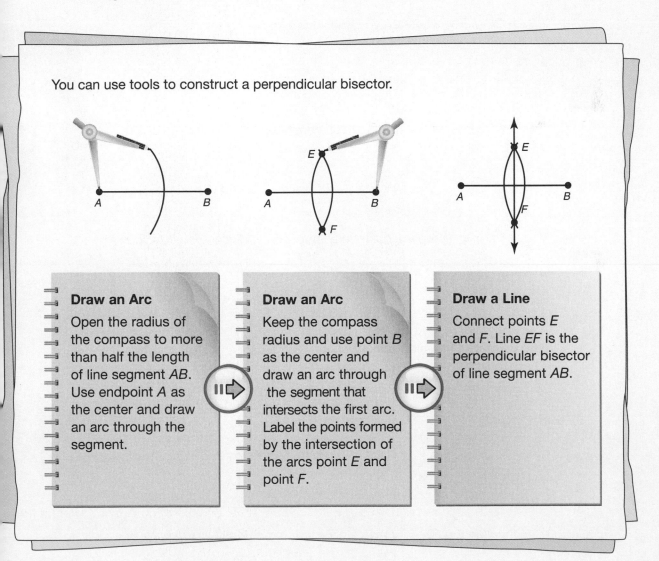

You can use tools to construct a perpendicular bisector.

Draw an Arc

Open the radius of the compass to more than half the length of line segment AB. Use endpoint A as the center and draw an arc through the segment.

Draw an Arc

Keep the compass radius and use point B as the center and draw an arc through the segment that intersects the first arc. Label the points formed by the intersection of the arcs point E and point F.

Draw a Line

Connect points E and F. Line EF is the perpendicular bisector of line segment AB.

1. Construct the perpendicular bisector of $\overline{FG}$. Label the perpendicular bisector as $\overleftrightarrow{CD}$.

Why is it important to open the compass past the midpoint of the line segment to begin this construction?

G

F

2. Label the point at which $\overleftrightarrow{CD}$ intersects $\overline{FG}$ as point E.

3. If $\overleftrightarrow{CD} \perp \overline{FG}$, what can you conclude?

4. If $\overleftrightarrow{CD}$ bisects $\overline{FG}$, what can you conclude?

5. If $\overleftrightarrow{CD}$ is the perpendicular bisector of $\overline{FG}$, what can you conclude?

6. Construct the midpoint of $\overline{PQ}$.

P   Q

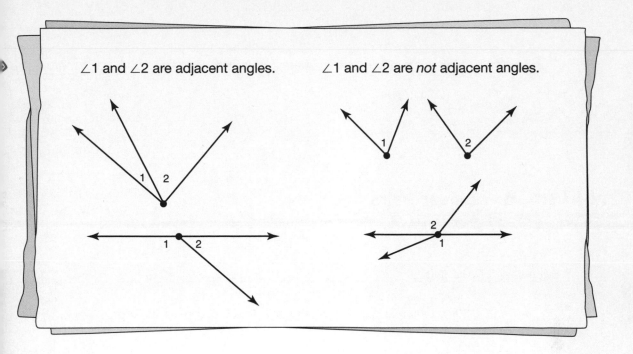

∠1 and ∠2 are adjacent angles.   ∠1 and ∠2 are *not* adjacent angles.

1. Describe *adjacent angles*.

2. Draw ∠2 so that it is adjacent to ∠1.

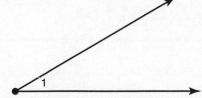

3. Is it possible to draw two angles that share a vertex, but do not share a common side? If so, draw an example. If not, explain your reasoning.

4. Is it possible to draw two angles that share a side, but do not share a vertex? If so, draw an example. If not, explain your reasoning.

Adjacent angles are two angles that share a common vertex and share a common side.

Problem 6   Linear Pairs

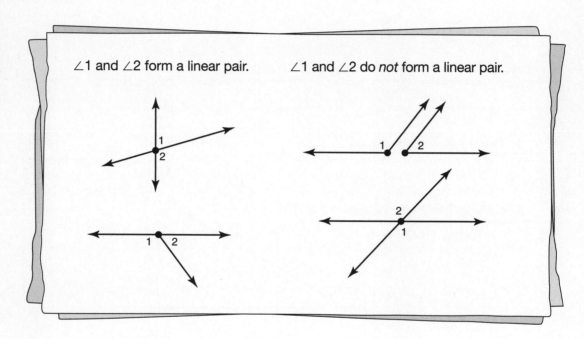

∠1 and ∠2 form a linear pair.   ∠1 and ∠2 do *not* form a linear pair.

1. Describe a linear pair of angles.

2. Draw ∠2 so that it forms a linear pair with ∠1.

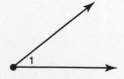

3. Name all *linear pairs* in the figure shown.

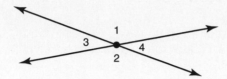

4. If the angles that form a linear pair are congruent, what can you conclude?

A **linear pair** of angles are two adjacent angles that have noncommon sides that form a line.

Problem 7   Vertical Angles

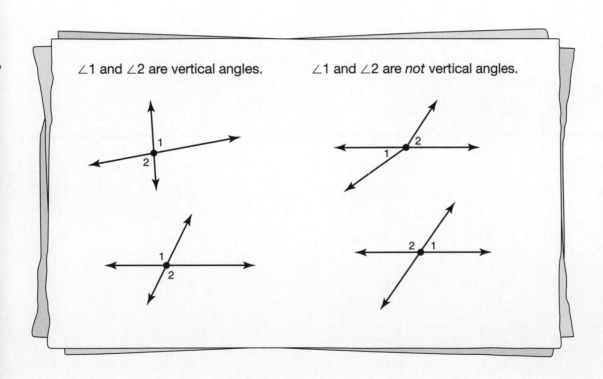

∠1 and ∠2 are vertical angles.   ∠1 and ∠2 are *not* vertical angles.

1. Describe *vertical angles*.

2. Draw ∠2 so that it forms a vertical angle with ∠1.

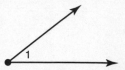

3. Name all vertical angle pairs in the diagram shown.

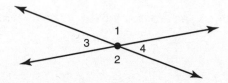

4. Measure each angle in Question 3. What do you notice?

Vertical angles are two nonadjacent congruent angles that are formed by two intersecting lines.

Be prepared to share your solutions and methods.

Key Terms

- geometry (9.1)
- protractor (9.1)
- compass (9.1)
- straightedge (9.1)
- sketch (9.1)
- draw (9.1)
- construct (9.1)
- geometric construction (9.1)
- point (9.1)
- line (9.1)
- plane (9.1)
- coplanar lines (9.1)
- skew lines (9.1)
- line segment (9.1)
- endpoints (9.1)

- arc (9.1)
- congruent line segments (9.1)
- congruent (9.1)
- intersection (9.1)
- ray (9.2)
- angle (9.2)
- sides of an angle (9.2)
- vertex (9.2)
- degrees (9.2)
- acute angle (9.2)
- right angle (9.2)
- obtuse angle (9.2)
- straight angle (9.2)
- congruent angles (9.2)
- bisect (9.2)

- angle bisector (9.2)
- supplementary angles (9.3)
- complementary angles (9.3)
- perpendicular (9.3)
- midpoint of a segment (9.3)
- segment bisector (9.3)
- perpendicular bisector (9.3)
- adjacent angles (9.3)
- linear pair (9.3)
- vertical angles (9.3)

9

9.1   Sketching and Drawing Geometric Figures

To sketch a geometric figure is to create the figure without the use of tools. To draw a geometric figure, the figure is created with the use of tools such as a ruler, straightedge, compass, or protractor. A drawing is generally more accurate than a sketch.

Example

A sketch and a drawing of the given figure are shown.

Sketch

Drawing

Your brain has a left and right side that usually work independently. Doing geometry helps both sides work together!

9.1 Constructing Circles

To construct a geometric figure, the figure is created using only a compass and a straightedge. A construction can also be called a geometric construction. A compass is a instrument used to construct circles and arcs by placing the steel point firmly into the paper and spinning the top of the compass around with the pencil point just touching the paper.

Example

The circle shown was constructed using $\overline{AB}$ as the radius and A as the center.

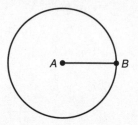

9.1 Constructing Arcs

An arc is a part of a circle. An arc can also be thought of as the curve between two points on the circle. Like circles, arcs are constructed using a compass.

Example

The arc shown was constructed using $\overline{CD}$ as the radius and D as the center.

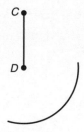

9.1 Constructing Duplicate Line Segments

Line segments that have the same length are called congruent line segments. Congruent means to have the same size, shape, and measure. A line segment can be duplicated by constructing an exact copy of the original.

Example

Line segment AB is a duplicate of $\overline{EF}$.

9.2 Drawing Angles with a Protractor

A protractor is a measuring device that can be used to approximate the measure of an angle. To draw an angle with a given measure, first draw one side of the angle using a straightedge. Next, align the bottom of the protractor with this side and align the center of the protractor with the endpoint of the side. Finally, place a mark at the given angle measure and draw the second side of the angle with a straightedge.

Example

This is an example of a 35° angle.

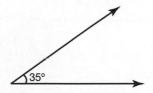

9.2 Constructing Duplicate Angles

Congruent angles are two or more angles that have equal measures. An angle can be duplicated by constructing an exact copy of the original angle.

Example

Angle B has been constructed to be congruent to $\angle A$.

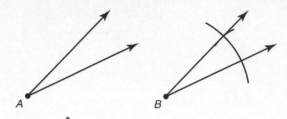

9.2 Constructing Angle Bisectors

An angle bisector is a ray through the vertex of an angle that divides the angle into two congruent angles. A compass and a straightedge can be used to construct the angle bisector of a given angle.

Example

The bisector of $\angle B$ has been constructed.

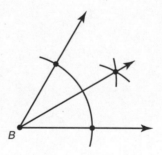

9.3 Calculating the Complement of an Angle

Two angles are complementary angles if the sum of their measures is equal to 90°. To calculate the complement of a given angle, subtract that angle's measure from 90°.

Example

The measure of an angle that is complementary to an angle whose measure is 24° is 90°−24°, or 66°.

Calculating the Supplement of an Angle

Two angles are supplementary angles if the sum of their measures is equal to 180°. To calculate the supplement of a given angle, subtract that angle's measure from 180°.

Example

The measure of an angle that is supplementary to an angle whose measure is 103° is 180°−103°, or 77°.

9

Constructing a Perpendicular

Two lines, line segments, or rays are perpendicular if they intersect to form 90° angles.

Example

A line that is perpendicular to the given line through point A has been constructed.

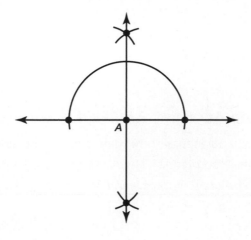

9.3 Constructing Perpendicular Bisectors and Midpoints

The midpoint of a segment is a point that divides the segment into two congruent segments. A perpendicular bisector is a line, line segment, or ray that intersects the midpoint of a line segment at a 90° angle.

Example

The perpendicular bisector of $\overline{BC}$ has been constructed. The midpoint of $\overline{BC}$ is D.

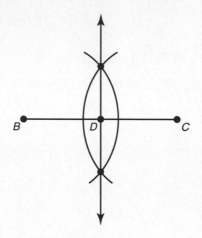

9.3 Classifying Adjacent Angles, Linear Pairs, and Vertical Angles

Two angles are adjacent if they share a common vertex and a common side and have no interior points in common. A linear pair of angles consists of two adjacent angles that have non-common sides that form a line. Vertical angles are two non-adjacent angles that are formed by two intersecting lines.

Example

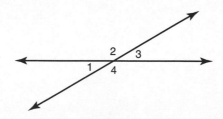

∠1 and ∠2 are adjacent angles, ∠2 and ∠3 are adjacent angles, ∠3 and ∠4 are adjacent angles, and ∠4 and ∠1 are adjacent angles.

∠1 and ∠2 form a linear pair, ∠2 and ∠3 form a linear pair, ∠3 and ∠4 form a linear pair, ∠4 and ∠1 form a linear pair.

∠1 and ∠3 are vertical angles, and ∠2 and ∠4 are vertical angles.

10 TRIANGLES

Triangles are interesting shapes. The triangle is a shape you'll often see in bridges and other buildings that need to be really sturdy.

10

PULLING A ONE-EIGHTY!

10.1

Triangle Sum, Exterior Angle, and Exterior Angle Inequality Theorems

Learning Goals

In this lesson, you will:

▶ Prove the Triangle Sum Theorem.

▶ Explore the relationship between the interior angle measures and the side lengths of a triangle.

▶ Identify the remote interior angles of a triangle.

▶ Identify the exterior angle of a triangle.

▶ Explore the relationship between the exterior angle measures and two remote interior angles of a triangle.

▶ Prove the Exterior Angle Theorem.

▶ Prove the Exterior Angle Inequality Theorem.

Key Terms

▶ Triangle Sum Theorem

▶ remote interior angles of a triangle

▶ Exterior Angle Theorem

▶ Exterior Angle Inequality Theorem

10

The measures of all the angles of a triangle equal 180°, right? And no triangle can have more than one right angle or obtuse angle, right?

Well, yes to both, unless you're talking about a spherical triangle. A spherical triangle is a triangle formed on the surface of a sphere. The sum of the measures of the angles of this kind of triangle is *always* greater than 180°. Spherical triangles can have two or even three obtuse angles or right angles.

The properties of spherical triangles are important to a certain branch of science. Can you guess which one?

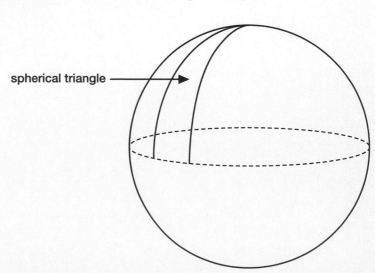

spherical triangle ⟶

Problem 1   Triangle Interior Angle Sums

1. Draw any triangle on a piece of paper. Tear off the triangle's three angles. Arrange th[e] angles so that they are adjacent angles. What do you notice about the sum of these three angles?

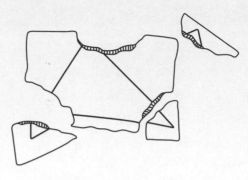

The **Triangle Sum Theorem** states that the sum of the measures of the interior angles of triangle is 180°.

Problem 2   Analyzing Triangles

1. Draw an acute triangle that is not an equiangular triangle. Measure each interior angl[e] and label the angle measures in your diagram.

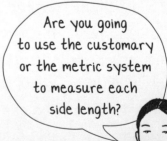

Are you going to use the customary or the metric system to measure each side length?

a. Measure the length of each side of the triangle. Label the side lengths in your diagram.

b. The longest side of the triangle lies opposite which interior angle?

c. The shortest side of the triangle lies opposite which interior angle?

2. Draw an obtuse triangle. Measure each interior angle and label the angle measures in your diagram.

10

    a. Measure the length of each side of the triangle. Label the side lengths in your diagram.

    b. The longest side of the triangle lies opposite which interior angle?

    c. The shortest side of the triangle lies opposite which interior angle?

3. Draw a right triangle. Measure each interior angle and label the angle measures in your diagram.

a. Measure each side length of the triangle. Label the side lengths in your diagram.

b. The longest side of the triangle lies opposite which interior angle?

c. The shortest side of the triangle lies opposite which interior angle?

4. The measures of the three interior angles of a triangle are 57°, 62°, and 61°. Describe the location of each side with respect to the measures of the opposite interior angles without drawing or measuring any part of the triangle.

a. longest side of the triangle

b. shortest side of the triangle

5. List the side lengths from shortest to longest for each diagram.

a.

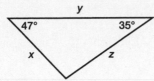

b.

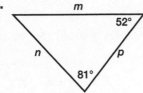

c.

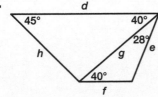

If two angles of a triangle have equal measures, does that mean their opposite sides are also congruent?

Use the diagram shown to answer Questions 1 through 11.

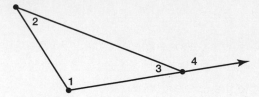

1. Name the interior angle(s) of the triangle.

2. Name the exterior angle(s) of the triangle.

3. What did you need to know to answer Questions 1 and 2?

4. What does $m\angle 1 + m\angle 2 + m\angle 3$ equal? Explain your reasoning.

5. What does $m\angle 3 + m\angle 4$ equal? Explain your reasoning.

6. Why does $m\angle 1 + m\angle 2 = m\angle 4$? Explain your reasoning.

7. Consider the sentence "The location of the buried treasure is on a remote island." What does the word "remote" mean?

8. Angle 4 is an exterior angle of a triangle and $\angle 1$ and $\angle 2$ are interior angles of the same triangle. Why would $\angle 1$ and $\angle 2$ be referred to as "remote" interior angles with respect to the exterior angle?

The **remote interior angles of a triangle** are the two angles that are non-adjacent to the specified exterior angle.

9. Rewrite $m\angle 4 = m\angle 1 + m\angle 2$ using the terms *sum, remote interior angles of a triangle*, and *exterior angle of a triangle*.

10. The diagram was drawn as an obtuse triangle with one exterior angle. If the triangle had been drawn as an acute triangle, would this have changed the relationship between the measure of the exterior angle and the sum of the measures of the two remote interior angles? Explain.

11. If the triangle had been drawn as a right triangle, would this have changed the relationship between the measure of the exterior angle and the sum of the measures of the two remote interior angles? Explain.

The relationship between the measure of an exterior angle of a triangle, such as $\angle 4$, and the sum of the measures of the two remote interior angles of a triangle, such as $\angle 1$ and $\angle 2$, is an important theorem in the study of geometry.

The **Exterior Angle Theorem** states that the measure of the exterior angle of a triangle is equal to the sum of the measures of the two remote interior angles of the triangle.

12. What can you conclude about the figure shown using the Exterior Angle Theorem?

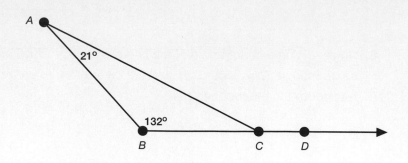

13. What can you conclude about the figure shown using the Exterior Angle Theorem?

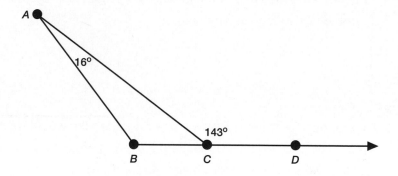

14. What can you conclude about the figure shown using the Exterior Angle Theorem?

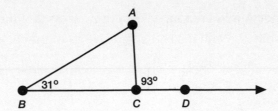

15. Solve for *x* in each diagram.

a.

b.

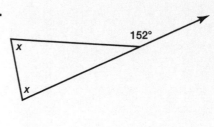

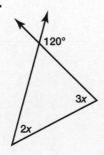

c.

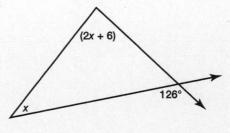

d.

Another important geometry theorem related to the Exterior Angle Theorem is called the Exterior Angle Inequality Theorem.

The **Exterior Angle Inequality Theorem** states that the measure of an exterior angle of a triangle is greater than the measure of either of the remote interior angles of the triangle.

16. What can you conclude about this figure using the Exterior Angle Inequality Theorem?

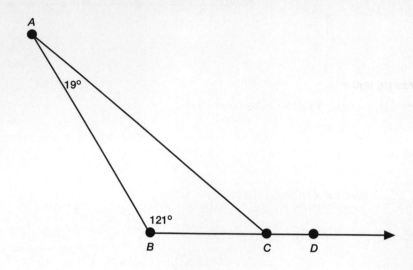

17. How does the Exterior Angle Inequality Theorem relate to the Exterior Angle Theorem?

Be prepared to share your solutions and methods.

10.2 TRIANGLE CONSTRUCTION I

Constructing Triangles

Learning Goal

In this lesson, you will:

- Construct triangles to determine uniqueness.

Possibly the most infamous triangle in the world is the Bermuda Triangle. This ; a triangle-shaped area east of the United States covering the Caribbean ;lands, and it is one of the most heavily traveled shipping lanes in the world.

eginning in the 1950s, newspapers began reporting about strange events in the ermuda Triangle—from sunken ships to downed planes to bizarre visions. People lamed these events on just about anything you can think of—UFOs, sea monsters, ven the lost continent of Atlantis. Have you heard of strange events occurring in ne Bermuda Triangle? Do you think there is some scientific explanation for bad vents occurring in this area?

Problem 1 A Triangle Given Two Line Segments

Two polygons are congruent if they are the same shape and size.

1. Construct a triangle using the two line segments shown. Write the steps.

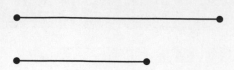

Remember to draw a starter line first.

2. Use a protractor to measure each angle and a ruler to measure each side.

3. Classify the triangle based on the measures of the angles and the lengths of the sides.

4. Compare the triangle that you constructed with the triangles that your classmates constructed. What do you observe? Why?

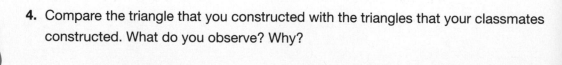

Problem 2 A Triangle Given Three Angles

1. Construct a triangle using the three angles shown. Write the steps.

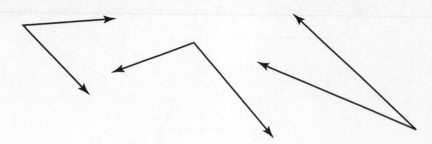

2. Use a protractor to measure each angle and a ruler to measure each side.

3. Classify the triangle based on the measures of the angles and the lengths of the sides.

4. Compare the triangle that you constructed with the triangles that your classmates constructed. What do you observe? Why?

1. Construct a triangle using one line segment and two angles shown. Write the steps.

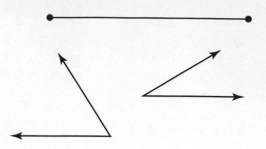

2. Use a protractor to measure each angle and a ruler to measure each side.

3. Classify the triangle based on the measures of the angles and the lengths of the sides.

4. Compare the triangle that you constructed with the triangles that your classmates constructed. What do you observe? Why?

alk the Talk

Based on each description, determine if you can create a unique triangle. Write an X for each description in the appropriate column.

Triangle Description	Unique Triangle	Not a Unique Triangle
given 2 line segments		
given 3 line segments		
given 3 angles		

 Be prepared to share your solutions and methods.

10

10.3 TRIANGLE CONSTRUCTION II

Congruent Figures and Constructing Congruent Triangles

Learning Goals

In this lesson, you will:

▶ Define congruent figures.

▶ Determine whether figures are congruent.

▶ Determine whether triangles are congruent.

▶ Construct congruent triangles.

Key Terms

▶ geometric figures

▶ congruent geometric figures

▶ corresponding sides

▶ corresponding angles

▶ included angle

▶ included side

10

Giorgio Vasari was an Italian writer and painter. He once told the story of a great painter named Cimabue (pronounced chee-ma-boo-eh) who hired the striving young artist, Giotto, as an apprentice. Vasari once wrote about how Giotto drew a fly so real-looking on the face of a painting that Cimabue mistakenly tried many times to brush it off. And once, when asked to demonstrate his skill as an artist, Giotto painted, it is said, such a perfect circle that those who looked on it could not believe it was drawn without a compass. Can you draw a perfect circle?

Problem 1 Congruent Figures

Geometric figures are figures composed of lines, line segments, points, lines, rays, angles, and arcs. **Congruent geometric figures** are figures that have exactly the same size and shape, which means that each part of one figure is congruent to each corresponding part of the other figure.

1. Draw a figure that is congruent to the figure shown. Remember that you may use yo measuring instruments, including your ruler and protractor.

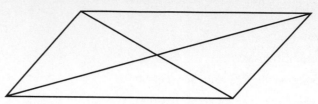

2. Use the figures shown to answer each question.

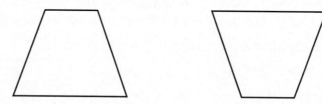

   a. Label all of the vertices on each figure.

   b. List each angle in each figure. Then, determine and label the measure of each angle

c. Determine and label the measure of each side in each figure in millimeters.

3. Are these two figures congruent? Why or why not?

Problem 2 Congruent Triangles

You know that triangles have three sides, or line segments, and three angles. Triangles are named by using their three vertices and the triangle symbol, △. It does not matter which letter you list first when naming a triangle. For example, you can name the triangle shown as △ABC, △ACB, △CBA, △BCA, or △BAC.

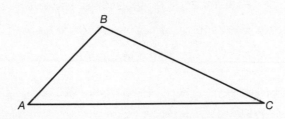

1. List the sides of △ABC with their lengths in millimeters.

Did you include the line segment symbol when you listed the sides?

2. List the angles of △ABC with their degree measure.

3. Draw △DEF ≅ △ABC using your geometry tools.

As you saw, it is not important which vertex you list first when naming a triangle. It is, however, important which vertex you list first when stating that two triangles are congruent. Parts of congruent triangles that are congruent to each other are called corresponding parts of congruent triangles. The corresponding parts of congruent triangles are corresponding sides and corresponding angles. **Corresponding sides** are sides that have the same relative positions in geometric figures. **Corresponding angles** are angles that have the same relative positions in geometric figures.

> In the congruence statement △ABC ≅ △DEF,
> - vertex A is first and corresponds to vertex D,
> - vertex B is second and corresponds to vertex E,
> - and vertex C is last and corresponds to vertex F.

4. Use the congruence symbol to show the corresponding sides that are congruent in these triangles.

5. Use the congruence symbol to show the corresponding angles that are congruent in these triangles.

6. Without drawing congruent triangles, write the corresponding sides and corresponding angles for the congruency statement △HOW ≅ △SEA.

1. Construct a triangle given the three line segments using the starter line provided. Make sure at least one person in your group starts with each of the different sides.

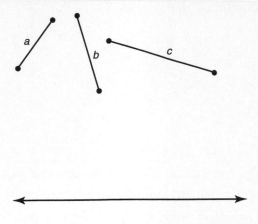

10

2. Compare the triangle you constructed with the triangles the other students in your group constructed. What do you notice?

3. Construct a triangle given the two sides and the *included angle* using the starter line provided. An **included angle** is the angle whose sides are made up of the specified sides of the triangle. Have half the members of your group begin the construction with the first side and the other half begin the construction with the second side.

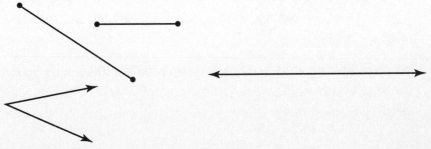

4. Compare the triangle you constructed with the triangles the other students in your group constructed. What do you notice?

5. Construct a triangle given two angles and the *included side* using the starter line provided. An **included side** is the side between the two specified angles of the triangle. Have half the members of your group begin the construction with the first angle and the other half begin the construction with the second angle.

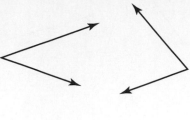

So, there are ways to tell if two triangles are congruent without measuring all their sides and angles.

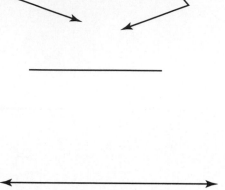

6. Compare the triangle you constructed with the triangles the other students in your group constructed. What do you notice?

Talk the Talk

In the last two lessons, you have learned different ways to create triangles. Depending on what you are given to start, you and your classmates created either multiple triangles or a unique triangle.

In the graphic organizer on the next page, list the three ways you can create multiple triangles and the three ways you can create a unique triangle, depending on what sides o angles you are given.

Be prepared to share your solutions and methods.

10

10

10.4 PASTA ANYONE?
Triangle Inequality Theorem

Learning Goals

In this lesson, you will:

► Explore the relationships between the side lengths of a triangle and the measures of its interior angles.

► Prove the Triangle Inequality Theorem.

Key Term

► Triangle Inequality Theorem

10

Mathematics often deals with things that are impossible. It is impossible to write the square root of 2 as a rational number. It is impossible to divide by 0. What other things in mathematics are impossible?

The same can be said for triangles. As you have learned, there are certain things a triangle needs to be a triangle. If those things are not met, then it is impossible for the figure to be a triangle. Can you name what those needs are?

Problem 1   Side and Angle Relationships

1. Draw a scalene triangle. Measure each side and angle.

    a. The largest interior angle of the triangle lies opposite which side?

    b. The smallest interior angle of the triangle lies opposite which side?

2. Draw an isosceles triangle that is not an equiangular triangle. Measure each side and angle.

    a. The largest interior angle(s) of the triangle lies opposite which side(s)?

    b. The smallest interior angle(s) of the triangle lies opposite which side(s)?

3. Draw an equilateral triangle. Measure each side and angle.

   a. The largest interior angle of the triangle lies opposite which sides?

   b. The smallest interior angle of the triangle lies opposite which side?

4. The lengths of the sides of a triangle are 4 cm, 5 cm, and 6 cm. Describe the location of each angle with respect to the lengths of the opposite sides without drawing or measuring any part of the triangle. Explain your reasoning.

   a. largest interior angle

   b. smallest interior angle

5. A side of a triangle decreases in measure and the other sides remain the same length. Describe what happens to the angle opposite the side.

6. A side of a triangle increases in measure and the other sides of the angle remain the same length. Describe what happens to the angle opposite the side.

10

Problem 2   Who is Correct?

Sarah claims that any three lengths will determine three sides of a triangle. Sam does not agree. He thinks some combinations will not work. Who is correct? Remember, you need one counterexample to disprove a statement.

You only need one counterexample to disprove a statement.

Sam then claims that he can just look at the three lengths and know immediately if they will work. Sarah is unsure. She decides to explore this for herself.

Help Sarah by working through the following activity.

To begin, you will need a piece of strand pasta (like linguine). Break the pasta at two random points so the strand is divided into three pieces.

1. Try to form a triangle from your three pieces of pasta.

2. Measure each of your three pieces of pasta in centimeters.

3. Collect and record your classmates' measurements.

Piece 1 (cm)	Piece 2 (cm)	Piece 3 (cm)	Forms a Triangle? (yes or no)

4. How many students are in your class?

5. How many students' pasta pieces formed a triangle when the three pieces were connected end to end?

Is there a way we can always tell if three side lengths will form a triangle?

6. How many students' pasta pieces did not form a triangle when the three pieces were connected end to end?

7. Examine the lengths of the pasta pieces that did form a triangle. Compare them with the lengths of the pasta pieces that did not form a triangle. What observations can you make?

8. Under what conditions is it possible to form a triangle?

9. Under what conditions is it impossible to form a triangle?

10. Based upon your observations, determine if it is possible to form a triangle using segments with the following measurements. Explain.

    a. 2 cm, 5.1 cm, 2.4 cm

    b. 9.2 cm, 7 cm, 1.9 cm

The rule that Sam was using is known as the Triangle Inequality Theorem.

The **Triangle Inequality Theorem** states that the sum of the lengths of any two sides of a triangle is greater than the length of the third side.

Determine whether it is possible to form a triangle using each set of segments with the given measurements. Explain your reasoning.

1. 3 in., 2.9 in., 5 in.

2. 4 m, 5.1 m, 12.5 m

3. 10 yd, 5 yd, 21 yd

4. 112 mm, 300 mm, 190 mm

5. 8 ft, 9 ft, 11 ft

6. 7.4 cm, 8.1 cm, 9.8 cm

7. 13.8 km, 6.3 km, 7.5 km

8. 20.2 in., 11 in., 8.2 in.

In each of the following, you are given the length of the two shortest sides of a triangle. What can you conclude about the length of the third side?

9. 10 m, 8 m

10. 14 in., 20 in.

11. 6 cm, 9 cm

12. 12 ft, 7 ft

13. 11 cm, 3 cm

14. 9 mm, 13 mm

15. Kaitlin noticed that a map of a triangular hiking route said that the entire hike was exactly 6 miles long. If each of the three connecting trails is a whole-number of mile long, how long is each trail? Explain how you determined your answer.

16. Angela needs a ladder to repair a second-story window. The window is 12 feet off th ground. Because there are bushes near the house, she must place the bottom of the ladder 5 feet from the edge of the house. Using the Triangle Inequality Theorem, determine the range of heights her ladder should have.

Be prepared to share your solutions and methods.

Key Terms

- Triangle Sum Theorem (10.1)
- remote interior angles of a triangle (10.1)
- Exterior Angle Theorem (10.1)

- Exterior Angle Inequality Theorem (10.1)
- geometric figures (10.3)
- congruent geometric figures (10.3)
- corresponding sides (10.3)

- corresponding angles (10.3)
- included angle (10.3)
- included side (10.3)
- Triangle Inequality Theorem (10.4)

10.1 Using the Triangle Sum Theorem

The Triangle Sum Theorem states: "The sum of the measures of the interior angles of a triangle is 180°."

Example

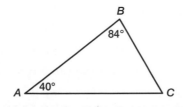

$$m\angle A + m\angle B + m\angle C = 180°$$
$$40° + 84° + m\angle C = 180°$$
$$m\angle C = 180° - (40° + 84°)$$
$$m\angle C = 180° - 124°$$
$$m\angle C = 56°$$

Using your hands to create things while learning helps your brain to learn new tasks. So there is a reason you had to construct all those triangles!

10.1 Exploring the Relationship between Interior Angle Measures and Side Lengths in Triangles

In a triangle, the length of each side is directly related to the size of the angle opposite th side. The longest side in a triangle lies opposite the largest angle. The shortest side in a triangle lies opposite the smallest angle. If two or more angles in a triangle are congruent then the sides which lie opposite those angles will also be congruent.

Example

In the triangle, side *b* is the longest side because it lies opposite the greatest angle. Side is the shortest side because it lies opposite the least angle.

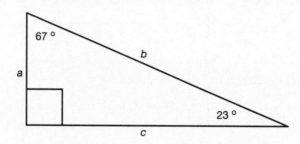

10.1 Using the Exterior Angle Theorem

The Exterior Angle Theorem states: "The measure of an exterior angle of a triangle is equ to the sum of the measures of the two remote interior angles of the triangle."

Example

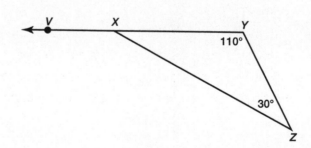

$m\angle VXZ = m\angle Y + m\angle Z$
$m\angle VXZ = 110° + 30°$
$m\angle VXZ = 140°$

Constructing Triangles

A triangle consists of three sides, or line segments, and three angles. You can construct congruent triangles if you know one of the following:

- the measures of the three sides
- the measures of two sides and the included angle
- the measures of two angles and the included side

Example

The triangle shown was constructed using the given sides.

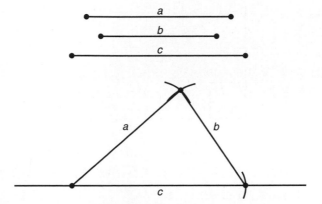

To construct the triangle, a horizontal starter line was drawn first. Next, one endpoint of line segment c was drawn on the starter line. The length of given line segment c was then measured with a compass and the compass was used to construct an arc that intersected the starter line. A point was drawn at the intersection of the arc and the starter line to indicate the other endpoint of side c. Next, the length of given line segment a was measured with the compass and an arc was drawn using this length. The length of given line segment b was then measured with the compass and an arc was drawn to intersect with the previous arc. A point was drawn at the intersection point of the two arcs. Finally, the remaining two sides were constructed using a straightedge.

10.3 Determining Whether Figures Are Congruent

Congruent geometric figures are figures that have exactly the same size and shape. This means that each part of one figure is congruent to each part of the other figure. A ruler and a protractor can be used to measure the sides and angles of two figures to determine whether they are congruent.

Example

 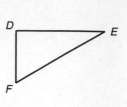

$\triangle ABC \cong \triangle EDF$, because

$\overline{AB} \cong \overline{ED}$, $\overline{BC} \cong \overline{DF}$, $\overline{AC} \cong \overline{EF}$, $\angle A \cong \angle E$, $\angle B \cong \angle D$, and $\angle C \cong \angle F$.

10.3 Identifying Corresponding Sides and Angles Given a Congruence Statement

Parts of congruent triangles that are congruent to each other are called corresponding parts of congruent triangles. Corresponding sides are sides that have the same relative positions in geometric figures. Corresponding angles are angles that have the same relative positions in geometric figures. In a congruence statement, the corresponding vertices of the congruent figures are located in the same relative position.

Example

Given that $\triangle CBA \cong \triangle XYZ$:

$\overline{CB} \cong \overline{XY}$, $\overline{BA} \cong \overline{YZ}$, $\overline{CA} \cong \overline{XZ}$, $\angle C \cong \angle X$, $\angle B \cong \angle Y$, $\angle A \cong \angle Z$

Using the Triangle Inequality Theorem

The Triangle Inequality Theorem states: "The sum of the lengths of any two sides of a triangle is greater than the length of the third side."

Example

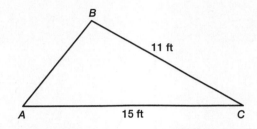

$AB < BC + AC$	$BC < AB + AC$	$AC < AB + BC$
$AB < 11 + 15$	$11 < AB + 15$	$15 < AB + 11$
$AB < 26$	$-4 < AB$	$4 < AB$

So, AB must be greater than 4 feet and less than 26 feet. (A length cannot be negative, so disregard the negative number.)

11 SCALE DRAWINGS AND SCALE FACTOR

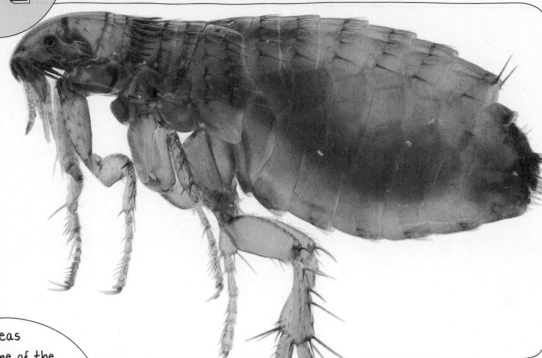

Fleas are some of the animal kingdoms most amazing athletes. Though they are on average only $\frac{1}{16}$ ch long, they can leap up to even inches vertically and irteen inches horizontally. This helps them attach emselves to warm-blooded hosts, such as people, dogs, or cats.

11

11

BIGGER AND SMALLER

Scale Drawings, Scale Models, and Scale Factors

Learning Goals

In this lesson, you will:

▶ Use scale models to calculate measurements.

▶ Use scale factors to enlarge and shrink models.

Key Term

▶ scale factor

Some professional basketball players can jump really high to dunk the ball on a 0-foot-tall goal. But those athletes have got nothing on fleas. These parasitic sects, which spend their time trying to suck the blood from other animals, can mp as high as seven inches.

hat doesn't sound impressive unless you know that a flea is only about $\frac{1}{16}$ inch ng, which means that a flea can jump more than 100 times its own length!

you could jump like a flea, how high could you jump? What tall buildings could ou leap in a single bound?

11

Problem 1   Scale Drawings

1. Emma enrolled in a sailing class. This diagram of a sailboat is on the first page of her text.

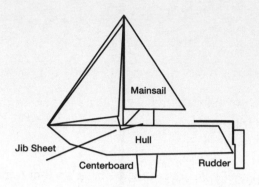

She decided to enlarge the diagram on a separate piece of paper as shown.

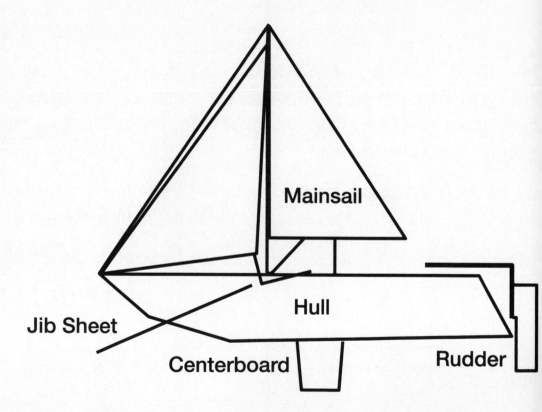

2. Determine the geometric shape that best describes each part of the sailboat.

- Mainsail
- Hull
- Centerboard
- Jib Sheet
- Rudder

3. Use a centimeter ruler to measure the dimensions of the Mainsail in the text and the Mainsail in Emma's enlargement of the diagram.

4. The ratio of side lengths in the scaled figure to those of the original figure is called the **scale factor.** Determine the scale factor Emma used to create the enlargement of the diagram.

A blueprint is an example of a scale drawing that represents a larger structure. The blueprint shown will be used for the construction of a new house.

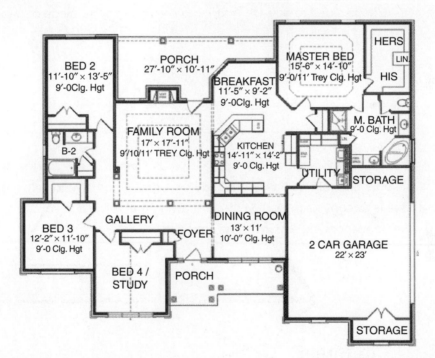

5. Use a centimeter ruler to determine the scale factor used to create the blueprint.

Scale drawings are also used to display small objects. The illustration shown is an artist's drawing of an oxygen atom. It shows eight electrons orbiting a nucleus that contains eight protons (dark spheres) and eight neutrons (light spheres). If the drawing were to scale, the nucleus would be invisible, 10,000 times smaller than it is currently drawn. A more sophisticated depiction of the electrons would show them as pulsating, three-dimensional wavelike clouds rather than little orbiting bullets.

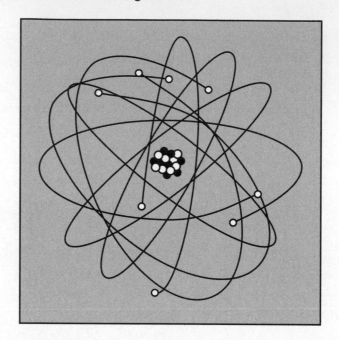

One method for enlarging or shrinking a drawing is to use a grid. The drawing of the sailboat that follows has been made on a grid. Another grid with larger cells is drawn. The idea is to copy each portion of the drawing that is in each square of the original grid into the corresponding square of the new grid.

6. Use this method to enlarge the drawing.

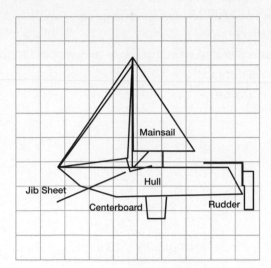

Problem 2   Scale Models

Scale models are also used for three-dimensional models.

1. A model of a C130 airplane has a scale of $\frac{1}{100}$.

  a. If the model plane is one foot long, how long is the actual plane?

  b. If the model's wingspan is 16 inches, how long is the actual wingspan?

  c. If the width of each of the model's propellers is 1.62 inches, how wide is an actual propeller?

  d. If the width of the actual tail is 52 feet 8 inches, what is the width of the tail in the model?

  e. If the height of the actual tail is 38 feet 5 inches, what is the height of the tail in the model?

11

2. This model of a barn has been constructed using a scale of 1 to 48.

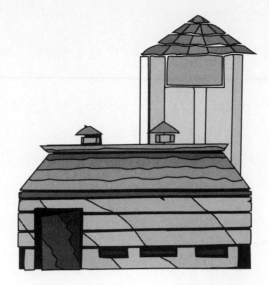

a. If the model's barn door is two and one quarter inches high, how high is the actual barn door?

b. If the model's silo is 18 inches high, how high is the actual silo?

c. The actual barn is 80 feet wide, 50 feet deep, and 60 feet to the roof. What are the dimensions of the model?

d. Suppose a dollhouse is built using a scale of 1 : 12. The actual house has 10 foot ceilings in all the rooms. How high are the ceilings in the dollhouse?

e. The porch on the dollhouse is 6 inches high. How high is the actual porch of the house?

 Be prepared to share your solutions and methods.

11

Learning Goal

In this lesson, you will

▶ Work with applications of similarity and scale factor.

Key Term

▶ aspect ratio

U p until the 1920s, movies did not have any sound with them. These silent films had what were known as intertitles to show dialogue and to tell the story being shown. These movies were far from silent, however. They were often played in a theater and live music was played to the action of the movie. Have you ever seen a silent film?

11

Problem 1 School Photos

When Timmons Photo Company prints photo packages, they include several sizes of photos that are all mathematically similar. The largest size is 12 in. × 16 in. This is read a "12 inches by 16 inches." The first measure is the width of the photo, and the second measure is the height of the photo.

16 in.

12 in.

1. Determine the other possible photo sizes that are mathematically similar.

a. 2 in. × _____

b. _____ × 8 in.

c. 3 in. × _____

d. _____ × 2 in.

e. 4 in. × _____

f. _____ × 3.5 in.

Problem 2 Aspect Ratios

An **aspect ratio** of an image is the ratio of its width to its height. Aspect ratios are used to determine the screen sizes for movie screens and televisions. Aspect ratios are written as two numbers separated by a colon (width : height).

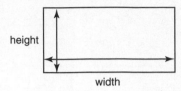

height

width

1. Before 1950, the aspect ratio of all motion pictures and standard definition televisions was 1.33 : 1. This meant that the screen was 1.33 times as wide as it was tall.

   a. Scale this ratio up to a ratio using only whole numbers.

   _____ : _____

   b. What did you use for your scale factor? Explain how you determined what scale factor to use.

2. After 1950, the movie industry wanted to create a different image than what was seen on television, so it adopted the widescreen ratios of 1.85 : 1, which was called the Academy Flat, and 2.35 : 1, which was called Panavision. Explain why these ratios are called widescreen ratios.

3. High definition televisions, or HDTVs, use an aspect ratio of 1.78 : 1. Written as a rat[io] using whole numbers, the HDTV aspect ratio is 16 : 9. Complete the table to show which similar television screen sizes are appropriate for showing TV shows and movies in high definition.

HDTV Sizes	
Width	**Height**
8 inches	
	18 inches
48 inches	
	3 feet
	4.5 feet

4.5 feet is 54 inches.

4. Complete the table to show which similar television screen sizes are appropriate for to show movies made in Panavision.

Panavision Sizes	
Width	**Height**
	1 foot
	6 feet
	12 feet
11.75 feet	
23.5 feet	
	20 feet

Problem 3   Flags of the World

Each country of the world has a flag that is designed to a specific ratio of height : length. All the flags of a particular country must be proportioned in the same ratio.

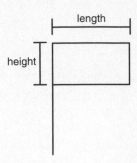

The table shown lists some countries and the height : length ratio of their flags.

	Countries		Ratio height : length
Group A	Bermuda Canada Ethiopia Jamaica	Libya New Zealand Nigeria	1 : 2
Group B	Liberia United States		10 : 19
Group C	China Congo Egypt France Greece India	Italy Japan Kenya Russia South Africa Spain	2 : 3
Group D	Iran Mexico		4 : 7
Group E	England Germany Haiti	Nicaragua Scotland Wales	3 : 5
Group F	Switzerland Vatican City		1 : 1

11

1. The sizes of flags are given in terms of height × length for each. State which group (A through F) each flag must belong to based on its ratio of height : length.

   a. 2 feet × 4 feet

   b. 10 feet × 15 feet

   c. 20 feet × 20 feet

   d. 12 feet × 21 feet

   e. 5 feet × 9.5 feet

   f. 1.5 feet × 2.5 feet

2. Which group of countries has square flags?

3. Which groups of countries have flags which are slightly different from 1 : 2?

roblem 4   Legoland

Legoland, California, has an area called Miriland, USA with all the famous U.S. buildings built to a 1 : 20 or 1 : 40 scale. One exception is the Empire State Building. The model of the Empire State Building is built using four different scales. The ground floors are built at a 1 : 20 scale to match the size of the model people on the street. The main body of the building is built at a 1 : 40 scale. It then changes to a 1 : 60 scale closer to the top of the model, and the very top tower is built at a 1 : 80 scale. The different scales at the higher levels of the model trick the eye into thinking that the building is much taller than it is. If you were to build a model of the Empire State Building using a 1 : 20 scale for the entire model, it would be over 62 feet tall versus the Legoland version, which is 20 feet tall!

1. Approximately how tall is the Empire State Building? Use the fact that a 1 : 20 scale model would be over 62 feet tall. Show and explain your work.

2. Complete the table to represent the heights of actual buildings and the heights of their models at a 1 : 20 scale.

Name of Building	Height of the Actual Building	Height of the Scale Model at a 1 : 20 Scale
Washington Monument Washington, D.C.	555.5 feet	
U.S. Capitol Building Washington, D.C.		4.4 meters
Willis Tower (formerly the Sears Tower) Chicago, Illinois	1451 feet	
Transamerica Pyramid San Francisco, CA	850 feet	
191 Peachtree Tower Atlanta, GA		13.25 m
Modis Tower Jacksonville, FL	163.07 m	

Problem 5 Gulliver's Travels

Maybe you have read or seen *Gulliver's Travels*, written by Jonathan Swift and published in 1726. In the story, Lemuel Gulliver visits two lands in his travels: Lilliput, the land of tiny people, and Brobdingnag, the land of the giants. The Lilliputians are $\frac{1}{12}$ of Lemuel's size, and the Brobdingnagians are 12 times his size.

1. Complete the measurements in the table to compare your world, which is the same as Lemuel's, with the worlds of the Lilliputians and the Brobdingnagians.

		Your World	Lilliput World	Brobdingnag World
a.	Pencil Length			
b.	Your Height			
c.	Math Book Length and Width			
d.	Your Foot Length			
e.	Paper Clip Length			
f.	Postage Stamp Length and Width			

Be sure to label your measurements.

1. The scale factor for a model car is 1 : 24. What does this mean?

2. The scale factor for a model train is 1 : 87. What does this mean?

Be prepared to share your solutions and methods.

11

11.3

NO GPS? BETTER GET THE MAP OUT!
Exploring Scale Drawings

Learning Goals

In this lesson, you will:

▶ Work with applications of similarity and scale factor.

▶ Use scale drawings and maps.

Key Term

▶ scale drawings

What do surveyors, mapmakers, architects, engineers, and builders all have in common? All of these people use *scale drawings*. **Scale drawings** are representations of real objects or places that are in proportion to the real objects or places they represent. The scale in a scale drawing is given as a ratio. Maps and blueprints are examples of scale drawings.

Why do you think scale drawings are important?

11

Problem 1   Scale Drawings

The purpose of a scale drawing is to represent either a very large or very small object.

The scale of a drawing might be written as:

$$1 \text{ cm} : 4 \text{ ft}$$

Drawing   Actual
Length   Length

This scale means that every 1 centimeter of length in the drawing represents 4 feet of the length of the actual object.

The scale of a map might look like this:

$$1 \text{ in.} : 200 \text{ mi}$$

Map   Actual
Distance   Distance

This scale means that every 1 inch of distance on the map represents 200 miles of actual distance.

1. Write a sentence to describe the meaning of each.

   a. A scale on a map is 1 in. : 2 ft

   b. A scale on a drawing is 1 cm : 4 cm

   c. A scale on a drawing is 2 in. : 1 in.

   d. A scale on a drawing is 1 cm : 1 cm.

Problem 2   A Map of Washington, D.C.

A partial map of Washington, D.C., is provided. A scale is included on the map.

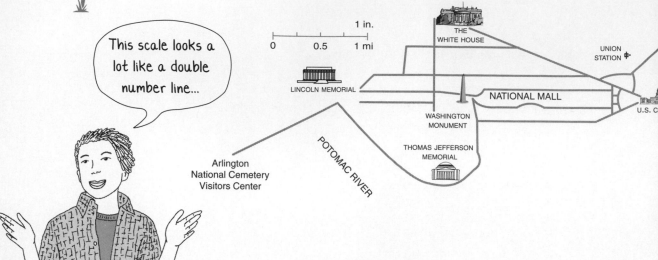

This scale looks a lot like a double number line...

1. Complete the table to help tourist groups plan their visits to our nation's capital.

Sights	Approximate Distance Using Roads and Paths
White House to Lincoln Memorial	
Lincoln Memorial to Arlington Cemetery (Visitor Center)	
Arlington Cemetery (Visitor Center) to Jefferson Memorial	
Jefferson Memorial to Washington Monument	
Washington Monument to U.S. Capitol	
U.S. Capitol to Union Station	

2. Why does it make sense to use roads and paths instead of measuring directly from one sight to the next sight?

3. Explain how you estimated the distances between sights.

4. Why are your answers approximate distances?

5. What is the total miles traveled between sights?

Problem 3   A Map of the United States

A map of the United States is shown. A scale is included on the map.

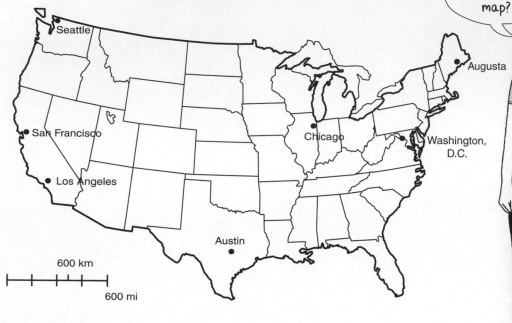

Seattle

Augusta

San Francisco

Chicago

Washington, D.C.

Los Angeles

Austin

600 km

600 mi

Why is this scale different from the one in the Washington D.C. map?

Determine the approximate distances between the locations. State the distances in miles and kilometers.

1. Washington, D.C., to San Francisco, California

2. Washington, D.C., to Seattle, Washington

3. Washington, D.C., to your state capital _____

4. Chicago, Illinois, to Los Angeles, California

5. Augusta, Maine, to Austin, Texas

6. Which is longer, a mile or a kilometer? How can you tell?

7. How many kilometers make one mile? Explain how you determined your answer.

8. How many days would it take to travel from Washington, D.C., to San Francisco, California, traveling at 60 miles per hour for 8 hours per day? Show your work.

9. Does your response to Question 8 seem realistic? Explain your reasoning.

11

Problem 4   Interpreting Scales

1. Which scale would produce the largest scale drawing of an object when compared to the actual object? Explain your reasoning.

1 in. : 25 in.

1 cm : 1 m

1 in. : 1 ft

2. Which scale would produce the smallest scale drawing of an object when compared to the actual object? Explain your reasoning.

1 in. : 10 in.

1 cm : 10 cm

1 mm : 1 m

3. The scale of a drawing is 6 cm : 1 mm. Is the scale drawing larger or smaller than the actual object or place? Explain your reasoning.

4. Given a scale of $\frac{5}{4}$, explain how you can tell whether the drawing is bigger or smaller than the actual object.

So since scales are ratios, you can write them in fraction form just like any other ratio.

5. In the 1989 movie *Honey I Shrunk the Kids*, a professor accidentally shrinks his kids to $\frac{1}{4}$ of an inch with a shrink ray. The kids then get accidentally sent out to the backyard. To the tiny kids, the backyard seems to have giant ants, giant bees, and grass as tall as trees!

> You can write a scale as actual length : drawing length. Just remember which value is which!

Each ant and bee were actually these sizes in real life:

	Length	**Height**	**Width**
Ant	12 mm	3 mm	1 mm
Bee	0.5 in.	0.25 in.	0.25 in.

The special effects team used a scale of 1 : 40 to create models of giant ants and bees. One unit of actual length corresponded to 40 units of length on each model. Complete the table to show the sizes of the models built by the team.

	Length	**Height**	**Width**
Ant			
Bee			

6. A microscope has a scale of 100 : 1. A microorganism appears to be 0.75 inch in length under the microscope.

a. How long is the microorganism? Show your work.

b. A microorganism is 0.085 millimeter long. How long will it appear under the microscope? Show your work.

7. A different microscope has a scale of 1000 : 1. An amoeba has a length of 25 millimeters under the microscope. What is the actual length of the amoeba? Show your work.

8. A 0.035-centimeter-long paramecium appears to be 17.5 millimeters long under a microscope. What is the power of the microscope? Show your work.

9. The height of a building in an architectural drawing is 12 inches. The actual height of the building is 360 feet. What is the scale of the drawing? Show your work.

10. A poster was enlarged and made into a billboard. The billboard was 20.5 feet by 36 feet. The scale used was 5 : 1. What was the size of the original poster? Explain your reasoning.

11. How do you determine the scale if a statue is 60 feet high and its scale drawing shows the height as 1 foot high?

12. Explain how to calculate the actual distance between two cities if you know the distance between them on a map and the scale of the map.

13. Draw a scale drawing of your math classroom. Give the dimensions of the room and the scale.

Remember, you will need to determine the actual size of the room before you can draw it to scale.

11

Problem 5   Blueprints

A blueprint is a technical drawing, usually of an architectural or engineering design. An example of a blueprint is shown.

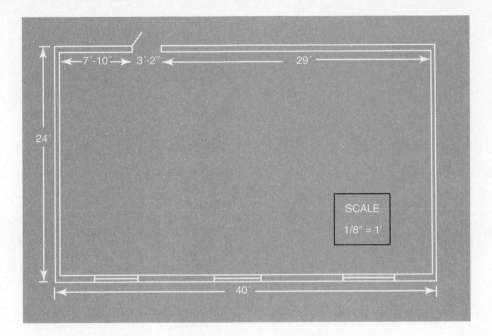

1. Design a courtyard for your school using this blueprint and the scale $\frac{1}{8}$ inch = 1 foot. Include:

   • features appropriate for a courtyard that would enhance the environment

   • features that would be popular for students, teachers, and parents

   • at least 10 features in the space provided (multiples of the same feature are acceptable)

   All features should be:

   • drawn to scale

   • positioned on the blueprint keeping scale in mind

   • drawn directly on the blueprint or cut out of paper and taped to the blueprint

   • labeled, either directly on the item or by using a key

Be prepared to share your solutions and methods.

11

11.4

HOUSES FOR OUR FEATHERED FRIENDS!

Creating Blueprints

Learning Goals

In this lesson, you will:

▶ Use scale drawings to create three-dimensional models.

▶ Use three-dimensional models to create blueprints.

The swallows of San Juan Capistrano are famous. They leave Argentina at about the end of October and arrive at the same church every year in California on March 19. How far do these birds travel to their summer vacations? Not far. Just 6000 miles! Do you think there are other creatures that travel long distances at different times of years? Do you think there are any other reasons animals would migrate from one part of the world to another?

11

Problem 1   Rectangular Wren Houses

Wren houses are built in several sizes and shapes. One example of a square wren house is shown.

1. Label the boards with appropriate measures.

WREN HOUSE

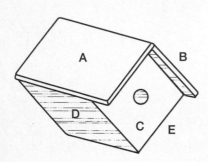

A	B	D	E

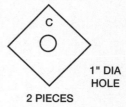

ALL MATERIAL IS 1/2" THICK

BACK PIECE MAY BE ATTACHED WITH 1" SCREWS
TO ALLOW FOR TAKING APART FOR CLEANING

C

1" DIA
HOLE

2 PIECES

2. One example of a rectangular wren house is shown.

Think about how tall and wide you want the birdhouse to be.

Draw the different boards used for this wren house.
Include measurements.

3. You can construct a birdhouse using only nails and a single 1 ft by 6 ft board.

Some of the measurements were not included. Label the boards and determine the unknown measurements.

(The front and back are made from two pieces.)

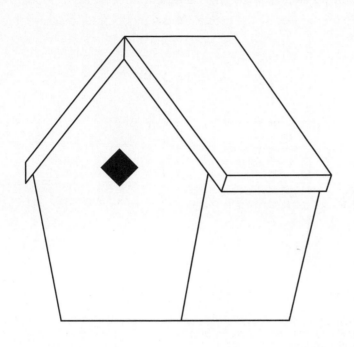

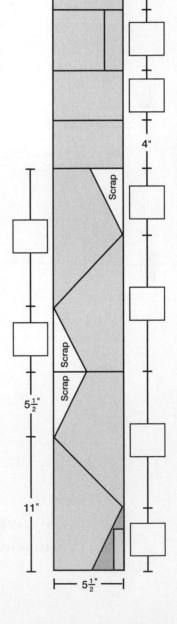

Problem 2 Design Your Own Bird Hotel!

Draw a scale model of a bird hotel. The hotel should have several rooms and separate openings such that each bird can enter its own room.

Create a blueprint that includes the measurements necessary to build the birdhouse and include the scale used to draw the model. You may be able to search the Internet for ideas.

11

Be prepared to share your solutions and methods.

Key Terms

▶ scale factor (11.1)

▶ aspect ratio (11.2)

▶ scale drawings (11.3)

11.1   Dilating Scale Drawings

Scale drawings are used to display very large or very small objects. Maps and blueprints are examples of scale drawings. The ratio of side lengths in the scaled figure to those of the original figure is called the scale factor. One way to dilate, or enlarge or shrink, a scale drawing is to use a grid.

Example

The drawing of the car is enlarged on the grid.

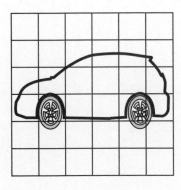
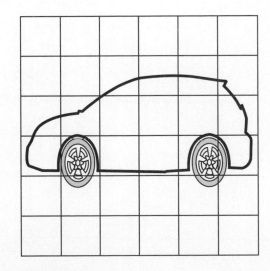

Did you like drawing these scale figures or do you like building things with your hands? If you do, the part of your brain that controls your fingers is much bigger than those who don't work with their hands!

11.1 Using Scale Models to Calculate Measurements

Scale models are three-dimensional dilations of actual objects. The scale factor can be used to calculate actual measurements.

Example

Suppose that a scale model of an Apache helicopter was constructed using a scale factor of $\frac{1}{48}$. The model is 3.5 inches tall, and each of the four rotating blades on an actual Apache helicopter is 300 inches long.

The height of an actual Apache helicopter is $3.5 \times 48 = 168$ inches, or $168 \div 12 = 14$ feet. Each blade on the model is $300 \times \frac{1}{48} = 6.25$ inches long.

1.2 Exploring Aspect Ratio

An aspect ratio of an image is the ratio of its width to its height. Aspect ratios are written as two numbers separated by a colon (width : height).

Example

Gwen has a photo that is 8 inches wide by 10 inches high. She would like to enlarge the photo into a poster that is 36 inches wide and has the same aspect ratio as the photo. First, the aspect ratio is determined by following the steps shown.

$$\text{aspect ratio} = \frac{8}{10}$$

$$= \frac{4}{5}$$

aspect ratio = 4 : 5.

Now that the aspect ratio is determined, you can calculate the height of the poster.

$$\frac{4}{36} = \frac{5}{x}$$

$$(4)(x) = (36)(5)$$

$$4x = 180$$

$$x = 45$$

poster = 36 in. $\times$ 45 in.

The poster will be 36 inches wide by 45 inches high.

11

11.3 Exploring Scale Drawings

Scale drawings are representations of real objects or places that are in proportion to the real objects or places they represent. The scale is given as a ratio of drawing length to actual length.

Example

The height of the Statue of Liberty is 93 meters. Althea would like to create a scale model for her history class. The model must be no taller than 0.5 meters. Althea can determine the scale of her model by using the maximum height of her model and the height of the Statue of Liberty.

$$\frac{0.5}{93} = \frac{5}{930}$$

$$= \frac{1}{186}$$

Althea should build the model at a scale of 1 : 186.

11.3 Interpreting Scales

It can be determined if an actual object is larger or smaller than the drawing because scales are written as drawing length: actual length or $\frac{\text{drawing length}}{\text{actual length}}$. If the drawing length value is larger, then the real object is smaller and vice versa.

Example

A photo is enlarged using a scale of 8 : 1. The resulting photo is 8" × 10". The original photo was 1" × $1\frac{1}{4}$".

$8 \div 8 = 1$
$10 \div 8 = 1.25$

Drawing a Blueprint Given an Illustration of an Object

A blueprint is a technical drawing, usually of an architectural or engineering design. Measurements in a blueprint are drawn to scale.

Example

A blueprint is drawn for the dog house shown.

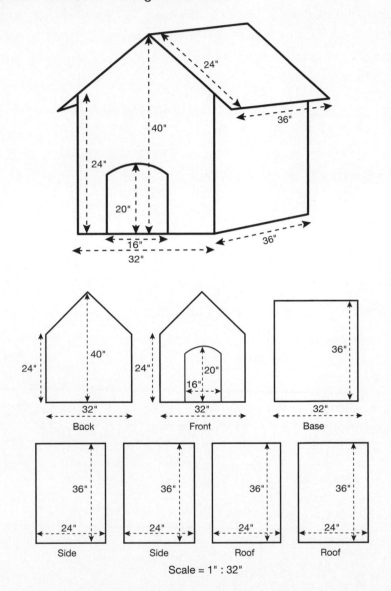

11

12 CIRCLES

Crop circles are really cool, and they come in all kinds of complex designs. The designs usually can only be seen from the air. As nice as they are though, they are still harmful to crops.

12

587

12

12.1 INTRODUCTION TO CIRCLES

Circle, Radius, and Diameter

Learning Goals

In this lesson, you will:

- Define circle.
- Identify the center, radius, and diameter of a circle.

Key Terms

- circle
- center of a circle
- radius of a circle
- diameter of a circle

You stop a friend in the hallway to ask about his or her weekend. As you are lking, another friend shows up and joins the conversation. Soon, another and en another and then another person joins in. Before long, your group will form a ape without even thinking about it. Your group will probably form a circle.

y and notice this the next time it happens—either to you or in another group. hy do you think people naturally form a circle when talking?

12

Problem 1 Definition of a Circle

Everyone can identify a circle when they see it, but defining a circle is a bit harder. Can you define a circle without using the word *round*? Investigating how a circle is formed w help you mathematically define a circle.

Step 1: In the middle of the space below, draw a point and label the point B.

Step 2: Use a centimeter ruler to locate and draw a second point that is exactly 5 cm from point B. Label this point A.

Step 3: Locate a third point that is exactly 5 cm from point B. Label this point C.

Step 4: Repeat this process until you have drawn at least ten distinct points that are each exactly 5 cm from point B.

1. How would you describe this collection of points in relation to point B?

2. How many other points could be located exactly 5 cm from point B?

3. All of the points you have drawn are on the same plane. Are there other points that are 5 cm from point B that are not on this plane? If so, describe their location.

4. The shape formed by connecting all points located 5 cm from point *B* on the same plane is two-dimensional. What is the name of this shape?

5. The solid formed by connecting all points located 5 cm from point *B* is three-dimensional. What is the name of this solid?

6. Define the term *circle* without using the word *round*.

roblem 2   Parts of a Circle

Use the circle shown to answer each question.

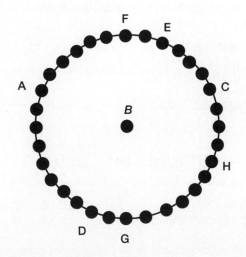

A **circle** is a collection of points on the same plane equidistant from the same point. The **center** of a **circle** is the point from which all points on the circle are equidistant. Circles are named by their center point.

  1. Name the circle.

The **radius of a circle** is a line segment formed by connecting a point on the circle and the center of the circle. The **diameter of a circle** is a line segment formed by connecting two points on the circle such that the line segments passes through the center point.

2. Identify a radius of the circle.

The plural of *radius* is *radii*.

3. Identify a diameter of the circle.

4. Are all radii of this circle the same length? Explain your reasoning.

5. What is the relationship between the length of a radius and the length of a diameter

Problem 3   Using Congruent Circles

Recall that congruent means "the same size and the same shape."

1. If Circle *A* is congruent to Circle *B*, what can you conclude about the lengths of the radii in Circle *A* and Circle *B*?

2. If Circle *A* is congruent to Circle *B*, what can you conclude about the lengths of the diameters in Circle *A* and Circle *B*?

3. Dione knows Circle *D* is congruent to Circle *E*. What is Dione's reasoning?

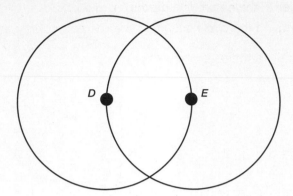

Problem 4   Circles Related to Equilateral Polygons

Mr. Graham was explaining to his students how circles are directly related to polygons. The class was discussing how circles do not have sides and polygons have sides, so it was not clear to them how circles and polygons had much of anything in common. Mr. Graham told his students to use only their compasses and try to discover a relationship.

1. Jeff discovered he could construct an equilateral triangle using two congruent circles. Jeff's drawing is partially shown.

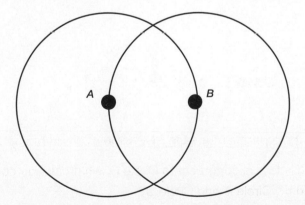

   Complete Jeff's work to show the equilateral triangle. Explain your reasoning.

2. Jackie said that she could construct an equilateral quadrilateral using three congrue[...]
circles. Jackie's work is partially shown.

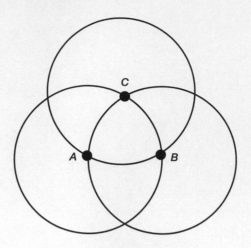

Complete Jackie's work to show the equilateral quadrilateral. Explain your reasoning[...]

3. Use your compass to construct a hexagon with all congruent sides.
Explain how you did it.

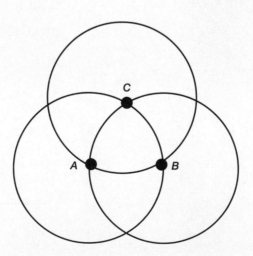

Two circles make the triangle. Three circles make the quadrilateral. How many circles will I need here?

12.2

BUT MOST OF ALL, I LIKE PI!

Circumference of a Circle

Learning Goals

In this lesson, you will:

▶ Measure the circumference of a circle.

▶ Explore the relationship between the diameter and the circumference of a circle.

▶ Write a formula for the circumference of a circle.

▶ Use a formula to determine the circumference of a circle.

Key Term

▶ pi

Beginning in about the 1970s, people in many different countries began reporting formations formed in fields, created by flattening down crops in certain ways. These came to be known as crop circles.

At first, people thought that weather or even aliens were creating these formations, but it turned out that groups of people would go into fields at night and create the crop circles themselves. Many of these formations are extremely complex and beautiful.

12

Problem 1   Measuring the Circumference of a Circle

Recall that the circumference of a circle is the distance around the circle.

Let's explore circles.

Use a string and a centimeter ruler to measure the radius and circumference of each circle.

1.

2.

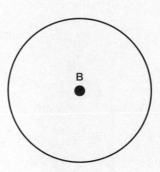

3.

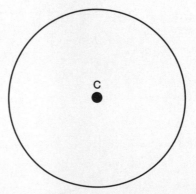

4.

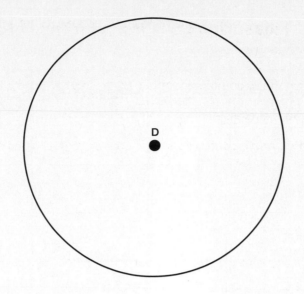

5.

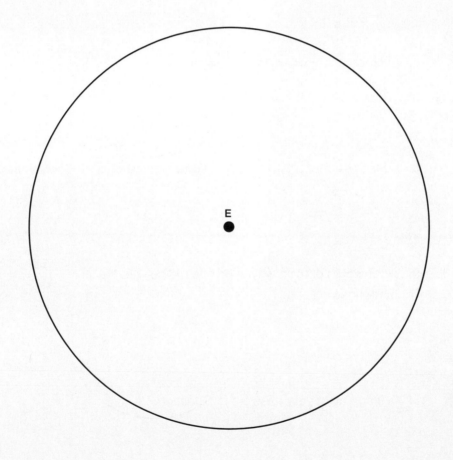

6. Record your measurements from Questions 1 through 5 in the table and complete the table.

Circle	Radius	Diameter	Circumference	Circumference / Diameter
Circle A				
Circle B				
Circle C				
Circle D				
Circle E				

7. Average the answers in the last column.

8. How does your answer to Question 7 compare to your classmates' answers?

9. What would explain why everyone did not get the same answer?

Do you see any patterns?

10. Average all of your answers to Question 7.

Problem 2   Construct Your Own Circles

Use a compass to construct five of your own circles and measure the radius and circumference of each circle.

   1.

   2.

   3.

12

4.

5.

12

6. Record your measurements in the table and complete the table.

Circle	Radius	Diameter	Circumference	Circumference/Diameter

7. Average the answers in the last column.

How does this table compare to the last one?

8. How does your answer to Question 7 compare to your classmates' answers?

9. Average all of your answers to Question 7.

10. What symbol is used to represent the ratio of the circumference of a circle to the diameter of the circle?

Problem 3 Circumference Formula

The number **pi** (π) is the ratio of the circumference of a circle to its diameter. That is,

$pi = \dfrac{circumference\ of\ a\ circle}{diameter\ of\ a\ circle}$ or $\pi = \dfrac{C}{d}$, where C is the circumference of the circle, and

d is the diameter of the circle. The number π has an infinite number of decimal digits that never repeat. Some approximations used for the exact value π are 3.14 and $\frac{22}{7}$.

1. Use this information to write a formula for the circumference of a circle, where d represents the diameter of a circle and C represents the circumference of a circle.

2. Rewrite the formula for the circumference of a circle, where r represents the radius of a circle and C represents the circumference of a circle.

3. The diameter of a circle is 4.5 centimeters. Compute the circumference of the circle using the circumference formula. Let $\pi = 3.14$.

4. The radius of a circle is 6 inches. Compute the circumference of the circle using the circumference formula. Let $\pi = 3.14$.

> Whenever you use 3.14 for pi all your answers are approximates.

5. The circumference of a circle is 65.94 feet. Compute the diameter of the circle using the circumference formula. Let $\pi = 3.14$.

6. The circumference of a circle is 109.9 millimeters. Compute the radius of the circle using the circumference formula. Let $\pi = 3.14$.

7. What is the minimum amount of information needed to compute the circumference of a circle?

 Be prepared to share your solutions and methods.

12

12.3 ONE *MILLION* SIDES!
Area of a Circle

How important are circles to architecture? Well this importance can be seen in many structures you have seen either in your towns or cities, and especially the many Gothic-style cathedrals in Europe. The architecture relies on buttresses, actually called flying buttresses which use circles.

To understand flying buttresses, you need to know what a buttress is. A buttress is architecture that is built against, or projecting from, a building's walls to offer support. However, the flying buttress uses the concepts of circles to offer significant support to a structure's roof and walls. In fact, when you see the flying buttresses in Gothic cathedrals, you can almost visualize a circle within each arch. Do you think that circles play vital roles in other architectural concepts?

12

Problem 1 Three Sides

Recall that the area formula for a triangle is $A = \frac{1}{2}bh$, where b is the length of the base o the triangle, and h is the height of the triangle.

An **inscribed circle** is a circle that fits exactly within the boundaries of another shape. It i the largest possible circle that will fit inside a plane figure.

Inscribed Circle D intersects the equilateral triangle at the midpoint of each side. The radius of the circle is r, and the length of each side of the triangle is s, as shown.

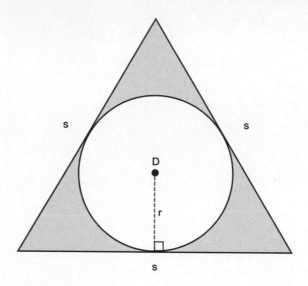

1. Draw three line segments from the center point of the circle to each corner of the triangle to form three congruent triangles. How is the radius of the circle, r, related to the three triangles?

2. Write a formula to describe the area of each of the three triangles you drew.

3. Write a formula to describe the area of the large triangle.

4. Write a formula to describe the perimeter of the large triangle.

You know the area of I small triangle, and 3 small triangles are all in the large triangle so...

5. Write a formula to describe the area of the large triangle in terms of the perimeter.

12

Inscribed Circle *D* intersects the square at the midpoint of each side. The radius of the circle is *r*, and the length of each side of the quadrilateral is *s*, as shown.

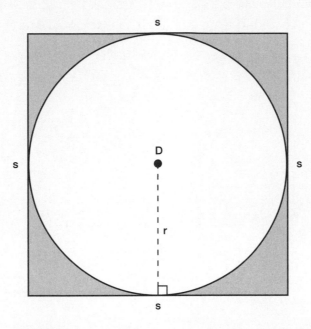

1. Draw four line segments from the center point of the circle to each corner of the quadrilateral to form four congruent triangles. How is the radius of the circle, *r*, related to the four triangles?

2. Write a formula to describe the area of each of the four triangles you drew.

3. Write a formula to describe the area of the quadrilateral.

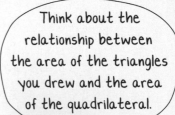

Think about the relationship between the area of the triangles you drew and the area of the quadrilateral.

4. Write a formula to describe the perimeter of the quadrilateral.

5. Write a formula to describe the area of the quadrilateral in terms of the perimeter.

Problem 3   Five Sides

Inscribed Circle *D* intersects the regular pentagon at the midpoint of each side. The radi
of the circle is *r*, and the length of each side of the pentagon is *s*, as shown.

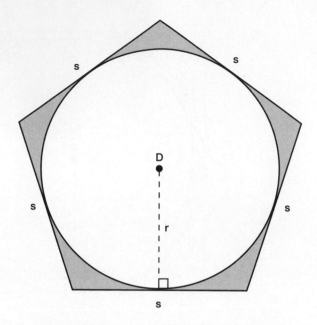

1. Draw five line segments from the center point of the circle to each corner of the
   pentagon to form five congruent triangles. How is the radius of the circle, *r*,
   related to the five triangles?

2. Write a formula to describe the area of each of the five
   triangles you drew.

3. Write a formula to describe the area of the pentagon.

> What
> relationship are
> you thinking about
> while describing
> the area of the
> pentagon?

4. Write a formula to describe the perimeter of the pentagon.

5. Write a formula to describe the area of the pentagon in terms of
   the perimeter.

Inscribed Circle *D* intersects the regular hexagon at the midpoint of each side. The radius of the circle is *r*, and the length of each side of the hexagon is *s*, as shown.

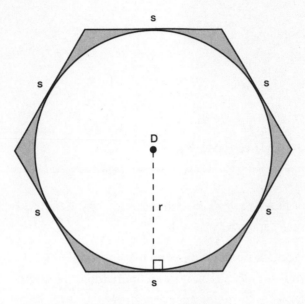

1. Draw six line segments from the center point of the circle to each corner of the hexagon to form six congruent triangles. How is the radius of the circle, *r*, related to the six triangles?

How did you use a similar strategy for each of these problems?

12

2. Write a formula to describe the area of each of the six triangles you drew.

3. Write a formula to describe the area of the hexagon.

4. Write a formula to describe the perimeter of the hexagon.

5. Write a formula to describe the area of the hexagon in terms of the perimeter.

Problem 5   A Million Sides

Use your answers to Question 5 in each of the last four problems to generalize.

I need to go back and look for a pattern.

1. If a regular polygon has one million sides, what formula could be used to compute the area of the polygon in terms of the perimeter?

2. If a regular polygon has *n* sides, what formula could be used to compute the area of the polygon in terms of the perimeter?

Problem 6   Getting It Together!

Recall that the area formula for a circle is $A = \pi r^2$, where r is the radius of the circle.

Recall that the circumference formula for a circle is $A = 2\pi r$, where r is the radius of the circle.

1. Use a centimeter ruler to measure the radius and sides of the regular polygons in Problems 1 through 4 and the circumference formula to complete the table. Use 3.14 for pi.

Regular Polygon/ Inscribed Circle	Side Length (s)	Perimeter (P)	Radius (r)	Circumference (C)
Equilateral Triangle				
Square				
Regular Pentagon				
Regular Hexagon				

2. What is the relationship between the perimeter of the regular polygon and the circumference of the inscribed circle as the number of sides of the regular polygon increases?

3. If the regular polygon had an infinitely large number of sides, how would you describe the perimeter of the regular polygon in relation to the circumference of the inscribed circle?

4. Use the measurements from Question 1 and the area formula to complete the table. Use 3.14 for pi.

Regular Polygon/ Inscribed Circle	Area of the Regular Polygon	Area of the Inscribed Circle	Area of the Shaded Region
Equilateral Triangle			
Square			
Regular Pentagon			
Regular Hexagon			

5. As the number of sides of the regular polygon increases, what do you notice about the area of the shaded region?

6. What is the relationship between the area of the regular polygon and the area of the inscribed circle as the number of sides of the regular polygon increases?

7. If the regular polygon had an infinitely large number of sides, how would you describe the area of the regular polygon in relation to the area of the inscribed circle?

You have established that the area of a regular polygon is half its perimeter times the radius of the inscribed circle or $A = \frac{1}{2}Pr$ in Problems 1 through 5.

You have observed that as the number of sides of the regular polygon increases, it approaches the shape of a circle in Problem 6.

Therefore, the formula $A = \frac{1}{2}Pr$ also applies to circles.

Technically, the perimeter of a circle is the same as the circumference of a circle.

Let's rephrase that: the area of a circle can be calculated using the formula $A = \frac{1}{2}Cr$.

You know that the circumference formula is $C = 2\pi r$.

Substitute an equivalent expression for C into the area formula and simplify. What do you notice?

$A = \frac{1}{2}Cr$

$C = 2\pi r$

AHA! Do you see how it works?

Think about all the relationships between these two formulas.

12

Be prepared to share your solutions and methods.

12

IT'S ABOUT CIRCLES!
Unknown Measurements

Learning Goals

In this lesson, you will:

▶ Use the area and circumference formulas to solve for unknown measurements.

▶ Use composite figures to solve for unknown measurements.

People have book circles—groups that meet to discuss books. There are circles of friends. There's the circle of life. Vicious circles. Come full circle. Going around circles. Circle the wagons.

Are there any other common phrases you can think of that use the word *circle*? Do you know what the phrase "circle the wagons" means?

Problem 1   Fencing

A friend gave you 120 feet of fencing. You decide to fence in a portion of the backyard for your dog. You want to maximize the amount of fenced land.

Draw a diagram, label the dimensions, and compute the maximum fenced area.

Assume the fence is free-standing and you are not using any existing structure.

Think about circles!

1. A circle is inscribed in a square. Determine the area of the shaded region.

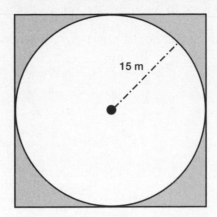

15 m

If you need to round then your area will be an approximation. Be sure to use the correct symbols.

2. Two small circles are drawn that touch each other, and both circles touch the large circle. Determine the area of the shaded region.

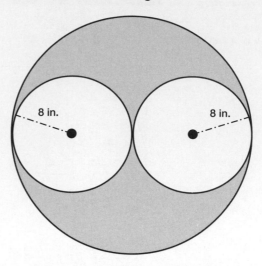

8 in.

8 in.

Jimmy and Matthew each said the area of the shaded region is about 402 sq in. Compare their strategies.

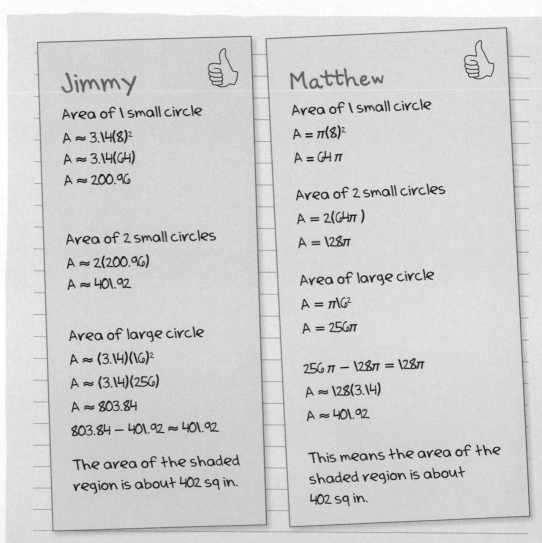

Jimmy 👍

Area of 1 small circle

$A \approx 3.14(8)^2$

$A \approx 3.14(64)$

$A \approx 200.96$

Area of 2 small circles

$A \approx 2(200.96)$

$A \approx 401.92$

Area of large circle

$A \approx (3.14)(16)^2$

$A \approx (3.14)(256)$

$A \approx 803.84$

$803.84 - 401.92 \approx 401.92$

The area of the shaded region is about 402 sq in.

Matthew 👍

Area of 1 small circle

$A = \pi(8)^2$

$A = 64\pi$

Area of 2 small circles

$A = 2(64\pi)$

$A = 128\pi$

Area of large circle

$A = \pi16^2$

$A = 256\pi$

$256\pi - 128\pi = 128\pi$

$A \approx 128(3.14)$

$A \approx 401.92$

This means the area of the shaded region is about 402 sq in.

a. What did Jimmy and Matthew do the same?

b. What was different about their strategies?

c. Which strategy do you prefer?

3. One medium circle and one small circle touch each other, and each circle touches the large circle. Determine the area of the shaded region.

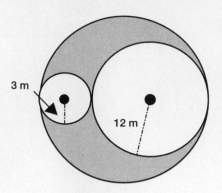

3 m

12 m

4. A rectangle is inscribed in a circle. Determine the area of the shaded region.

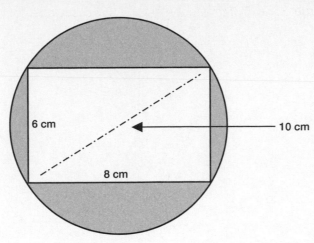

6 cm

10 cm

8 cm

How are your strategies to answer each of these questions the same?

5. A circle is inside a regular hexagon. Determine the area of the shaded region.

2 in.

2 in.

6 in.

6. Determine the area of the shaded region. All circles have the same radius of 10 inches.

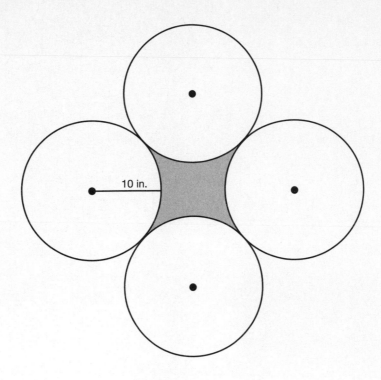

10 in.

Be prepared to share your solutions and methods.

12

12.1 **Defining a Circle and Its Properties**

A circle is a collection of points on the same plane equidistant from the same point. The center of a circle is the point from which all points on the circle are equidistant. Circles are named by their center point. The radius of a circle is a line segment formed by connecting a point on the circle and the center of the circle. The diameter of a circle is a line segment formed by connecting two points on the circle such that the line segment passes through the center point.

Example

Circle Z is shown. Point Z is the center of the circle. Line segment AZ is a radius of Circle Z. Line segment XY is a diameter of Circle Z.

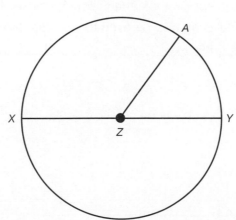

12

I like geometry more than algebra. But now I see how they're kind of connected.

12.2 Exploring the Relationship between the Diameter and Circumference of a Circle

Recall that the circumference of a circle is the distance around the circle. The number pi (π) is the ratio of the circumference of a circle to its diameter. That is, pi = $\frac{\text{circumference of a circle}}{\text{diameter of a circle}}$ or $\pi = \frac{C}{d}$, where C is the circumference of the circle and d is the diameter of the circle.

Example

The diameter of Circle M is 10 cm. The circumference of Circle M is 31.4 cm.

Circle	Radius	Diameter	Circumference	Circumferenc Diameter
M	5 cm	10 cm	31.4 cm	$\frac{31.4}{10} = 3.14$

12.2 Calculating the Circumference of a Circle

The circumference of a circle can be calculated using the formula $C = \pi d$ or the formula $C = 2\pi r$, where C represents the circumference of the circle, d represents the diameter o the circle, and r represents the radius of the circle. The value for π is often rounded to 3.14. The formula can also be used to calculate the diameter or radius of a circle when t circumference is known.

Example

The diameter of a circle is 54 cm. To calculate the circumference, use the formula $C = \pi$
$C = \pi d$
$\approx 3.14(54)$
≈ 169.56

The circumference of the circle is approximately 169.56 cm.

Using Circles Inscribed in Regular Polygons to Explore Area and Perimeter

An inscribed circle is a circle that fits exactly within the boundaries of another shape. It is the largest possible circle that will fit inside a plane figure. As the number of sides of the regular polygon increases, the perimeter of the regular polygon gets closer to the circumference of the inscribed circle. As the number of sides of the regular polygon increases, the area of the regular polygon gets closer to the area of the inscribed circle. The area of a regular polygon is half its perimeter times the radius of the inscribed circle.

Example

The radius of Circle T is equal to the height of each of the eight triangles in the octagon.

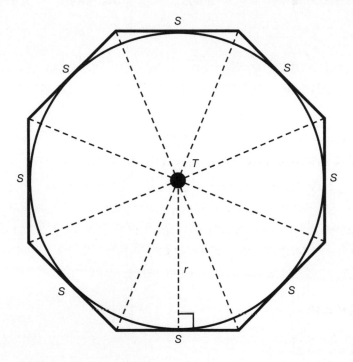

The area of each triangle is $A = \frac{1}{2}sr$.

The area of the octagon is $A = \frac{1}{2}sr \times 8$.

The perimeter of the octagon is $A = 8s$.

The area of the octagon in terms of its perimeter is $A = \frac{1}{2}Pr$.

12

12.3 **Exploring the Relationship between the Circumference and Area of a Circle**

The formula for the area of a regular polygon is $A = \frac{1}{2}Pr$, where P is the perimeter of the polygon and r is the radius of an inscribed circle. As the number of sides of a regular polygon increases, the shape of the polygon approaches the shape of a circle. Therefore the formula $A = \frac{1}{2}Pr$ can also be applied to circles.

Example

The perimeter or circumference of a circle can be calculated using the formula $C = 2\pi r$. By inserting the expression for the perimeter of a circle into the equation $A = \frac{1}{2}Pr$, it is determined that the area of a circle is $A = \frac{1}{2}(2\pi r)$ or $A = \pi r^2$.

12.4 **Using Area and Circumference Formulas to Solve for Unknown Measurements**

When solving problems involving circles with unknown measurements, the area and circumference formulas can be used to determine the measurements. A problem may require the use of both formulas to determine the answer.

Example

To calculate the area of a circle with a circumference of 15.7 meters, first determine the radius of the circle using the circumference formula.

$$C = 2\pi r$$
$$15.7 \approx 2(3.14)r$$
$$15.7 \approx 6.28r$$
$$\frac{15.7}{6.28} \approx \frac{6.28r}{6.28}$$
$$2.5 \text{ m} \approx r$$

The radius of the circle is 2.5 meters. Calculate the area of the circle using the area formula.

$$A = \pi r^2$$
$$A = \pi(2.5)^2$$
$$A = \pi(6.25)$$
$$A \approx 19.625 \text{ m}^2$$

A circle with a circumference of 15.7 meters has an area of approximately 19.625 square meters.

Using Composite Figures to Solve for Unknown Measurements

Many geometric figures are composites of two or more geometric shapes. When solving problems involving composite figures, it is often necessary to calculate the area of each geometric shape which composes the figure.

Example

A circle with a radius of 9 inches is inscribed inside a regular pentagon with side lengths of 13.1 inches. To calculate the area of the shaded region, subtract the area of the circle from the area of the pentagon.

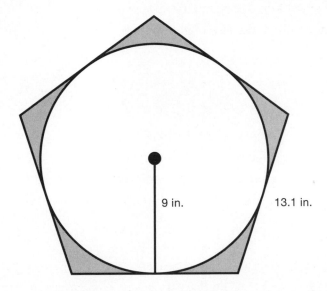

9 in. 13.1 in.

Calculate the area of the pentagon using the formula $A = \frac{1}{2}Pr$. The perimeter of the pentagon is 5(13.1) or 65.5 inches.

$A = \frac{1}{2}Pr$

$A = \frac{1}{2}(65.5)(9)$

$A = 294.75$ in.^{2}

Calculate the area of the circle.

$A = \pi r^2$

$A \approx (3.14)(9)^2$

$A \approx (3.14)(81)$

$A \approx 254.34$ in.^{2}

The area of the shaded region is approximately 294.75 − 254.34, or 40.41 square inches.

12

12

13 SLICING THREE-DIMENSIONAL FIGURES

When you show a cross section of a tree trunk, you will probably be able to see rings. A tree can add one ring each year, so counting the rings can tell you how old the tree is.

13

13

SLICING AND DICING
Slicing Through a Cube

Learning Goal

In this lesson, you will:

▶ Sketch, model, and describe cross-sections formed by a plane passing through a cube.

Key Term

▶ cross-section

You have probably seen cross-section models before. Biology teachers often use cross-section images of brains and other organs to show students the different parts inside. Cross-section models of ships are made to display the different levels and what happens on each level. Many dollhouses are just cross-sections. If they weren't, you couldn't see inside.

What other cross-section models have you seen before?

Problem 1 Time to Floss a Cube

In this chapter, you will use right rectangular prisms and right rectangular pyramids to determine the possible shapes formed when a plane passes through the solid. Recall tha a plane is a flat surface with two dimensions, length and width, and it extends infinitely ir all directions. A plane is the perfect tool to cut or slice into a geometric solid to reveal pa of the inside.

A **cross-section** of a solid is the two-dimensional figure formed by the intersection of a plane and a solid when a plane passes through the solid.

In this chapter, you will use clay to create a model for each geometric solid. Then, you w cut, or slice, the clay model to study possible cross-sections.

 Use clay to make a model of a cube like the one shown.

A plane can slice through a cube in a variety of ways. As a plane slices through a cube, a cross-section of the cube becomes viewable.

In this activity, you can use dental floss or a piece of thin wire to simulate a plane and sli through the clay cube such that the cross-section becomes viewable. If you make a slice and realize it is not what you wanted, just put the clay cube back together and try it agai

1. Slice through the middle of the clay cube in a direction perpendicular to the base.

   a. Describe the figure formed by the cross-section.

   b. If a different slice was made perpendicular to the base, but not through the middle of the cube, would the shape of the cross-section be the same or different? Explai

2. Slice through the middle of the clay cube in a direction parallel to the base.

    a. Describe the figure formed by the cross-section.

    b. If a different slice was made parallel to the base, but not through the middle of the cube, would the shape of the cross-section be the same or different? Explain.

3. What do you notice about all the cross-sections formed by the intersection of a plane that is either parallel or perpendicular to the base of a cube?

4. Put the cube back together and, this time, slice through the clay cube such that the cross-section formed at the intersection of the plane and the cube is a rectangle that is not a square. Describe where or how you sliced through the cube to create a rectangular cross-section.

If your slice is not what you want, just put the clay back together and try again.

5. Put the cube back together and, this time, slice through the clay cube such that the cross-section formed at the intersection of the plane and the cube is a triangle.

    a. Describe where or how you sliced through the cube to create a triangular cross-section.

    b. Compare your triangle with your classmates' triangles. Are all of the triangular cross-sections the same? Explain your reasoning.

    c. How can the cube be sliced to create an equilateral triangular cross-section?

6. Put the cube back together and, this time, slice through the clay cube such that the cross-section formed at the intersection of the plane and the cube is a pentagon. Describe where or how you sliced through the cube to create a pentagonal cross-sectio

7. Put the cube back together and, this time, slice through the clay cube such that the cross-section formed at the intersection of the plane and the cube is a hexagon.

   a. Describe where or how you sliced through the cube to create a hexagonal cross-section.

   b. Compare your hexagon with your classmates' hexagons. Are all of the hexagona cross-sections the same? Explain your reasoning.

   c. How can the cube be sliced to create a regular hexagonal cross-section?

8. Put the cube back together and, this time, slice through the clay cube such that the cross-section formed at the intersection of the plane and the cube is a parallelogram that is not a rectangle. Describe where or how you sliced through the cube to create parallelogram cross-section.

13

In this lesson, you were able to create all possible cross-sections of a cube. Let's now connect a name, diagram, and description for each cross-sectional shape of a cube.

1. Cut out all the representations on the following pages. Match each cross-sectional name with its diagram and description. Then tape the set of three in a single row in the graphic organizers.

Each row of your graphic organizer will include:

- a name for the cross-sectional shape.

- a diagram showing the cross-sectional shape.

- a description that explains how to create the cross-sectional shape.

Graphic organizers help me: Say It, See It, Talk about It.

I might say they help you: Name It, Visualize It, Describe It.

Be prepared to share your solutions and methods.

13

NAMES OF CROSS-SECTIONAL SHAPES

A square	A rectangle that is not a square	A triangle
A pentagon	A hexagon	A parallelogram that is not a rectangle

13

13

DIAGRAM OF CROSS-SECTIONAL SHAPES

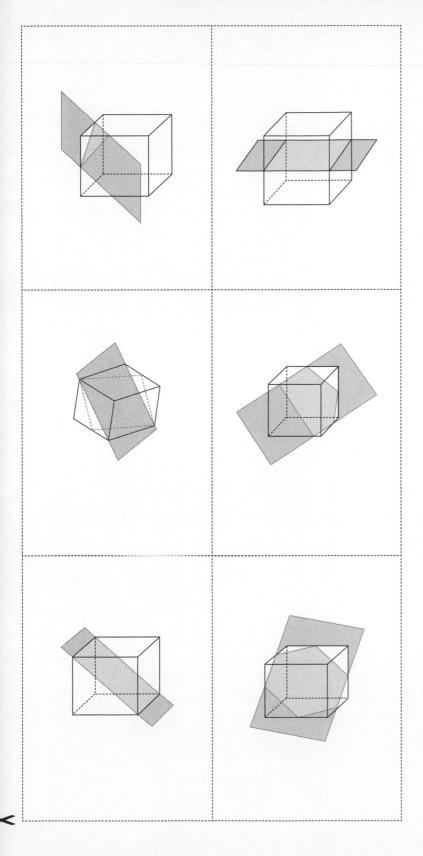

Think about the models you used.

13

DESCRIPTIONS OF CROSS-SECTIONAL SHAPES

The cube is sliced in a way such that the plane passes through two parallel edges where one edge is in the upper-left portion of the cube and the other edge is in the lower-right portion of the cube.

The cube is sliced in a way such that the plane passes through three intersecting edges, cutting off a corner of the cube.

The cube is sliced in a way such that the plane passes through the middle of the cube in a direction perpendicular to the base.

The cube is sliced in a way such that the plane passes through five of the six faces of the cube.

The cube is sliced in a way such that the plane passes through the cube at an angle not perpendicular to the base and not passing through any vertices.

The cube is sliced in a way such that the plane passes through all six faces of the cube.

13

CROSS-SECTIONAL SHAPES OF A CUBE

Name	Diagram	Explanation

CROSS-SECTIONAL SHAPES OF A CUBE

Name	Diagram	Explanation
		The cube is sliced in a way such that the plane passes through five of the six faces of the cube.
		The cube is sliced in a way such that the plane passes through all six faces of the cube.
		The cube is sliced in a way such that the plane passes through the cube at an angle not perpendicular to the base and not passing through any vertices.

13.2

THE RIGHT STUFF

Slicing Through Right Rectangular Prisms

Learning Goal

In this lesson, you will:

▶ Sketch, model, and describe cross-sections formed by a plane passing through a right rectangular prism.

Architects often make blueprints of floor plans for high-rise buildings. These floor plans are like cross-sections of the building, showing what you would be able to see if you sliced through the top of a floor horizontally and removed all the floors above it.

What might a floor plan look like if instead of slicing horizontally, you sliced vertically through the middle of a floor? Could you draw an example of what that might look like?

13

Problem 1   Time to Floss a Right Rectangular Prism

Use clay to make a model of a right rectangular prism that is not a cube, like the one shown. The bases of the rectangular prism are squares, and the lateral faces are rectangles.

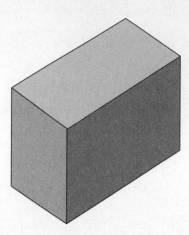

Will the cross-sections of a rectangular prism be similar to those of a cube?

A plane can slice through a right rectangular prism in a variety of ways. As a plane slices through a right rectangular prism, a cross-section of the prism becomes viewable.

In this activity, you can use dental floss or a piece of thin wire to simulate a plane and sli through the clay prism such that the cross-section becomes viewable. If you make a slic and realize it is not what you wanted, just put the clay prism back together and try it aga

1. Slice through the middle of the clay prism in a direction perpendicular to the base a parallel to the left and right face.

    a. Describe the figure formed by the cross-section.

    b. If a different slice was made perpendicular to the base and parallel to the left and right face, but not through the middle of the prism, would the shape of the cross-section be the same or different? Explain.

2. Slice through the middle of the clay prism in a direction parallel to the bases.

    a. Describe the figure formed by the cross-section.

    b. If a different slice was made parallel to the base, but not through the middle of th prism, would the shape of the cross-section be the same or different? Explain.

3. What do you notice about all the cross-sections formed by the intersection of a plane that is either parallel or perpendicular to the bases of a prism?

4. Put the prism back together and, this time, slice through the clay prism such that the cross-section formed at the intersection of the plane and the prism is a triangle.

    a. Describe where or how you sliced through the prism to create a triangular cross-section.

    b. Compare your triangle with your classmates' triangles. Are all of the triangular cross-sections the same? Explain your reasoning.

    c. How can the prism be sliced to create an equilateral triangular cross-section?

5. Put the prism back together and, this time, slice through the clay prism such that the cross-section formed at the intersection of the plane and the prism is a pentagon. Describe where or how you sliced through the prism to create a pentagonal cross-section.

6. Put the prism back together and, this time, slice through the clay prism such that the cross-section formed at the intersection of the plane and the prism is a hexagon. Describe where or how you sliced through the prism to create a hexagonal cross-section.

13

7. Put the prism back together and, this time, slice through the clay prism such that the cross-section formed at the intersection of the plane and the prism is a parallelogram that is not a rectangle. Describe where or how you sliced through the prism to create a parallelogram cross-section.

Talk the Talk

In this lesson, you were able to create all possible cross-sections of a right rectangular prism. Let's now connect a name, diagram, and description for each cross-sectional shape of a right rectangular prism.

1. Cut out all the representations on the following pages. Match each cross-sectional name with its diagram and description. Then, tape the set of three in a single row in the graphic organizers.

Each row of your graphic organizer will include:

- a name for the cross-sectional shape.
- a diagram that shows the cross-sectional shape.
- a description that explains how to create the cross-sectional shape.

13

NAMES OF CROSS-SECTIONAL SHAPES

A square	A rectangle that is not a square	A triangle
A pentagon	A hexagon	A parallelogram that is not a rectangle

13

13

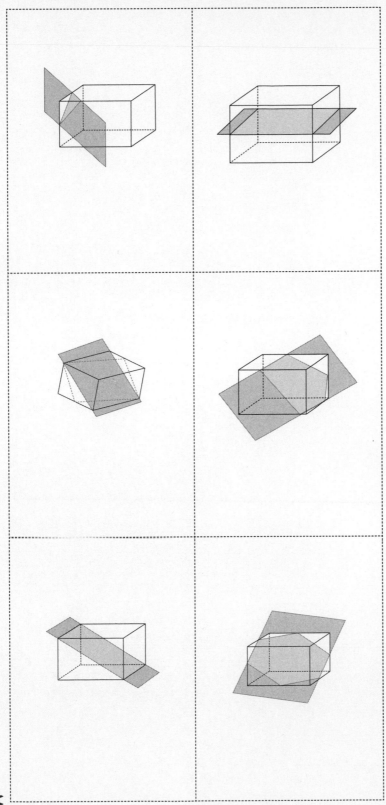

13

13

The right rectangular prism is sliced in a way such that the plane passes through two parallel edges where one edge is in the upper-left portion of the prism and the other edge is in the lower-right portion of the prism.

The right rectangular prism is sliced in a way such that the plane passes through three intersecting edges, cutting off a corner of the prism.

The right rectangular prism is sliced in a way such that the plane passes through the middle of the prism in a direction perpendicular to the base.

The right rectangular prism is sliced in a way such that the plane passes through five of the six faces of the prism.

The right rectangular prism is sliced in a way such that the plane passes through the prism at an angle not perpendicular to the base and not passing through any vertices.

The right rectangular prism is sliced in a way such that the plane passes through all six faces of the prism.

13

13

CROSS-SECTIONAL SHAPES OF A RIGHT RECTANGULAR PRISM

Name	Diagram	Explanation
		The right rectangular prism is sliced in a way such that the plane passes through the middle of the prism in a direction perpendicular to the base.
		The right rectangular prism is sliced in a way such that the plane passes through two parallel edges where one edge is in the upper-left portion of the prism and the other edge is in the lower-right portion of the prism.
		The right rectangular prism is sliced in a way such that the plane passes through three intersecting edges, cutting off a corner of the prism.

13

CROSS-SECTIONAL SHAPES OF A RIGHT RECTANGULAR PRISM

Name	Diagram	Explanation
		The right rectangular prism is sliced in a way such that the plane passes through five of the six faces of the prism.
		The right rectangular prism is sliced in a way such that the plane passes through all six faces of the prism.
		The right rectangular prism is sliced in a way such that the plane passes through the prism at an angle not perpendicular to the base and not passing through any vertices.

2. How do the cross-sections of a cube compare to the cross-sections of a rectangular .
   prism that is not a cube?

Be prepared to share your solutions and methods.

13

13.3

AND NOW ON TO PYRAMIDS

Slicing Through Right Rectangular Pyramids

<table>
<tr><td>

Learning Goal

In this lesson, you will:

▶ Sketch, model, and describe cross-sections formed by a plane passing through a right rectangular pyramid.

</td><td colspan="2">

Key Terms

</td></tr>
<tr><td></td><td>

▶ pyramid

▶ base of a pyramid

▶ lateral faces of a pyramid

▶ lateral edges of a pyramid

</td><td>

▶ vertex of a pyramid

▶ height of a pyramid

▶ regular pyramid

▶ slant height of a pyramid

</td></tr>
</table>

*P*yramid was one of the most popular American game shows in history. The show began in 1973 and was called *The $10,000 Pyramid*. Different versions of the game now aired all the way up to 2004, with the top prize increasing to $100,000.

The game involved 6 categories arranged in a triangular shape (or pyramid) and two contestants, one giving the clues and one trying to guess the name of the category to which the clues belonged.

So, for example, a contestant might be given the clues "head, feet, hands." The correct category in this case might be "parts of the body."

What category do these clues belong to?

Students, desks, a teacher, textbooks . . .

13

Problem 1 Time to Floss a Square Pyramid

A **pyramid** is a polyhedron formed by connecting one polygonal face to several triangular faces.

The **base of a pyramid** is a single polygonal face. Similar to prisms, pyramids are classified by their base.

The **lateral faces of a pyramid** are the triangular faces of the pyramid. All lateral faces of a pyramid intersect at a common point.

The **lateral edges of a pyramid** are the edges formed by the intersection of two lateral faces.

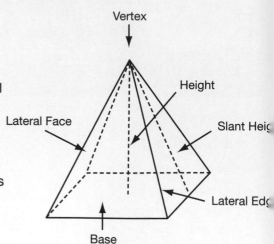

The **vertex of a pyramid** is the point formed by the intersection of all lateral faces.

The **height of a pyramid** is the perpendicular distance from the vertex of the pyramid to the base of the pyramid.

A **regular pyramid** is a pyramid in which the base is a regular polygon.

The **slant height of a regular pyramid** is the altitude of the lateral faces.

Use clay to make a model of a square pyramid, like the one shown. The base of the pyramid is a square, and the lateral faces are triangles.

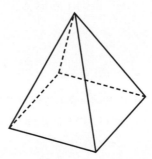

A plane can slice through a square pyramid in a variety of ways. As a plane slices through the pyramid, a cross-section of the pyramid becomes viewable.

In this activity, you can use dental floss or a piece of thin wire to simulate a plane and slice through the clay pyramid such that the cross-section becomes viewable. If you make a slice and realize it is not what you wanted, just put the clay pyramid back together and try it again.

1. Slice through the middle of the clay pyramid in a direction parallel to the square base.

   a. Describe the figure formed by the cross-section.

   b. How do the dimensions of the cross-section compare to the dimensions of the square base of the pyramid?

   c. If a different slice was made parallel to the base, but not through the middle of the pyramid, would the shape of the cross-section be the same or different? Explain.

2. Put the square pyramid back together and, this time, slice through the vertex of the clay pyramid in a direction perpendicular to the base.

   a. Describe the figure formed by the cross-section.

   b. If a different slice was made perpendicular to the base, but not through the vertex of the pyramid, would the shape of the cross-section be the same or different? Explain.

13

3. Put the pyramid back together and, this time, slice through the clay pyramid such th
the direction of the slice is neither parallel nor perpendicular to the base.

   a. Describe the figure formed by the cross-section.

   b. Compare your cross-section with your classmates' cross-sections. Are all of the cross-sections the same? Explain your reasoning.

   c. Is it possible to create an equilateral triangular cross-section?

Problem 2   Time to Floss a Right Rectangular Pyramid

Use clay to make a model of a right rectangular pyramid, like the one shown. The base of the pyramid is a rectangle that is not a square, and the lateral faces are triangles.

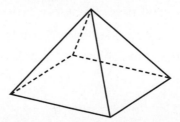

A plane can slice through a right rectangular pyramid in a variety of ways. As a plane slices through the pyramid, a cross-section of the pyramid becomes viewable.

In this activity, you can use dental floss or a piece of thin wire to simulate a plane and slic through the clay pyramid such that the cross-section becomes viewable. If you make a slice and realize it is not what you wanted, just put the clay pyramid back together and try it again.

1. Slice through the middle of the clay pyramid in a direction parallel to the rectangular base.

   a. Describe the figure formed by the cross-section.

   b. How do the dimensions of the cross-section compare to the dimensions of the rectangular base of the pyramid?

   c. If a different slice was made parallel to the base, but not through the middle of the pyramid, would the shape of the cross-section be the same or different? Explain.

2. Put the rectangular right pyramid back together and, this time, slice through the vertex of the clay pyramid in a direction perpendicular to the base.

   a. Describe the figure formed by the cross-section.

   b. If a different slice was made perpendicular to the base, but not through the vertex of the pyramid, would the shape of the cross-section be the same or different? Explain.

13

3. Put the pyramid back together and, this time, slice through the clay pyramid such th
the direction of the slice is neither parallel nor perpendicular to the base.

    a. Describe the figure formed by the cross-section.

    b. Compare your cross-section with your classmates' cross-sections. Are all of the cross-sections the same? Explain your reasoning.

    c. Is it possible to create an equilateral triangular cross-section?

    d. Is it possible to create a square cross-section?

4. How do the cross-sections of a square pyramid compare to the cross-sections of a right rectangular pyramid that does not have a square base?

Talk the Talk

In this lesson, you were able to create all possible cross-sections of a right rectangular pyramid. Let's now connect a name, diagram, and description for each cross-sectional shape of a right rectangular pyramid.

1. Cut out all the representations on the following pages. Match each cross-sectional name with its diagram and description. Then tape the set of three in a single row in the graphic organizer.

Each row of your graphic organizer will include:

- a name for the cross-sectional shape.
- a diagram that shows the cross-sectional shape.
- a description that explains how to create the cross-sectional shape.

NAMES OF CROSS-SECTIONAL SHAPES

A trapezoid	A rectangle that is not a square	A triangle

13

13

DIAGRAM OF CROSS-SECTIONAL SHAPES

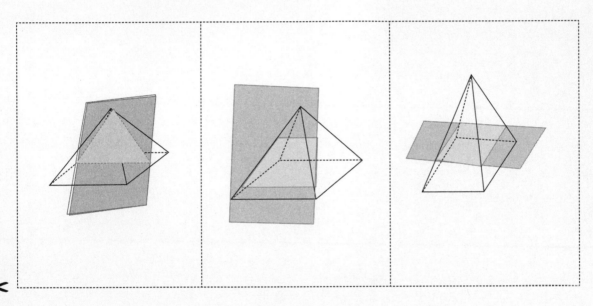

13

DESCRIPTIONS OF CROSS-SECTIONAL SHAPES

The pyramid is sliced in a way such that the plane passes through the middle of the clay pyramid in a direction perpendicular to the base.	The pyramid is sliced in a way such that the plane passes through the middle of the clay pyramid in a direction parallel to the base.	The pyramid is sliced in a way such that the direction of the slice is neither parallel nor perpendicular to the base.

✂

13

CROSS-SECTIONAL SHAPES OF A RIGHT RECTANGULAR PYRAMID

Name	Diagram	Explanation
		The pyramid is sliced in a way such that the direction of the slice is neither parallel nor perpendicular to the base.
		The pyramid is sliced in a way such that the plane passes through the middle of the clay pyramid in a direction parallel to the base.
		The pyramid is sliced in a way such that the plane passes through the middle of the clay pyramid in a direction perpendicular to the base.

13

13

13.4 BACKYARD BARBECUE
Introduction to Volume and Surface Area

Learning Goals

In this lesson, you will:

▶ Explore the volume of a solid.

▶ Explore the surface area of a solid.

▶ Create a net for a concave polyhedron.

Key Terms

▶ volume

▶ surface area

Where can you find the best barbecue? You might say that the answer to that question depends on where you go. But people from Kansas City or from anywhere in Texas will probably tell you that their barbecue is the best.

Have you had barbecue before? What's the best barbecue you've ever had?

13

Problem 1   Materials for a Patio

A landscaping company is installing a stone patio and a brick barbecue in the patio of a client's backyard. A model of the patio with the barbecue is shown.

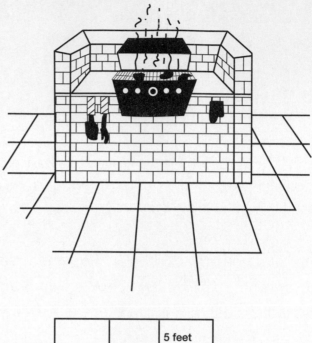

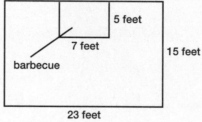

1. What is the area of the entire patio?

2. What is the area of the barbecue?

3. The patio will be covered with stone tiles that are 12-inch squares. The tiles will not be put under the barbecue. What is the area that will be covered with the tiles?

4. How many tiles will be needed for the job?

5. When the company orders materials, they always order an extra 10% of tiles because some of the tiles could break during shipping or some of the tiles could break while they are being cut to fit the patio. How many tiles should the company order?

6. Name the unit of measurement for the length of the patio.

7. Name the unit of measurement for the area of the patio.

8. How is the unit of measure used for the length different from the unit of measure for the area?

The **volume** of a solid three-dimensional object is the amount of space contained inside the object. Volume is described using cubic units of measure.

The **surface area** of a solid three-dimensional object is the total area of the outside surfaces of the solid. Surface area is described using square units of measure.

9. The barbecue will be made out of bricks that are 12 inches tall, 12 inches long, and 6 inches wide.

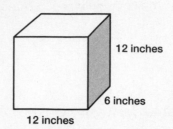

12 inches

6 inches

12 inches

The barbecue base will be 4 feet tall. When the bricks are laid, they must be staggered as much as possible so that the structure is solid. An overhead view and a side view of how the first layer of bricks might look are shown.

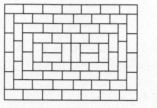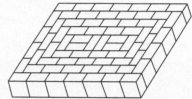

a. How tall is one layer of bricks in feet?

b. How many layers will be needed to complete the base?

10. Describe how you would use the length and the width of the barbecue base to determine the number of bricks that are needed for one layer of the base.

It's good to think about how you will do something before just jumping in.

11. Describe how you would determine the number of bricks that are needed to complete the base of the barbecue.

13

12. There are many different measurements involved in planning the construction of the barbecue.

    a. How many measurements are involved? Describe these measurements.

    b. A model of the barbecue base is shown. Label the base with the measurements you identified.

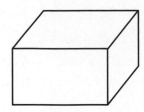

13. How many dimensions does volume involve?

14. Name the unit that is used to indicate the volume of the barbecue base.

15. Calculate the volume of the barbecue base.

16. Complete the statement and explain your reasoning.

Area is to square feet as volume is to_____.

13

17. When you consider the area of a two-dimensional plane figure like a polygon, the area is enclosed by one-dimensional line segments. When you consider the volume of a three-dimensional solid figure like the barbecue base, what kind of figures enclose the volume?

> We use square units to show we are measuring 2-D objects and cubic units to show we are measuring 3-D objects.

18. What is the shape of each side of the barbecue base?

19. How many outside surfaces does the barbecue base have? A model of the base is shown. Describe these surfaces.

13

Recall that the volume of a geometric solid is the amount of space contained inside the solid.

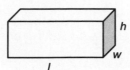

The volume, V, of a right rectangular prism is determined by the formula $V = l \times w \times h$, where l represents the length, w represents the width, and h represents the height of the prism as shown.

The diagram shown represents the entire barbecue.

1. Calculate the volume of the barbecue. Show all of your work.

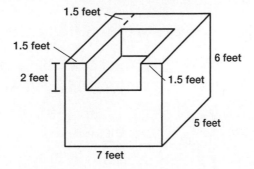

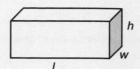

Recall that the surface area of a geometric solid is the total area of the outside surfaces the solid.

Each of the six rectangular sides of the prism is shown separately.

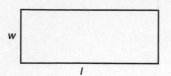

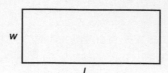

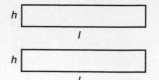

The surface area, SA, of a right rectangular prism is determined by the formula $V = 2lw + 2lh + 2wh$, where l represents the length, w represents the width, and h represents the height of the prism.

2. Calculate the surface area of the barbecue. Use diagrams to show all of your work.

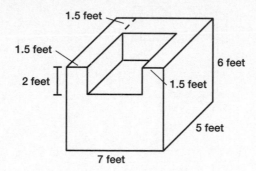

13

1. Can the volume of the barbecue ever be equal to the surface area of the barbecue? Explain your reasoning.

2. What does the volume of the barbecue tell you about the barbecue?

3. How can knowing the volume of the barbecue be helpful?

4. What does the surface area of the barbecue tell you about the barbecue?

5. How can knowing the surface area of the barbecue be helpful?

13

13.5

FAMOUS PYRAMIDS
Applying Volume and Surface Area Formulas

In the United States, there are two pyramids that were built to be used as sports arenas. One of the pyramids is the Walter Pyramid, located in Long Beach, California. The other pyramid is the Pyramid Arena, located in Memphis, Tennessee.

Pyramid Arena

Walter Pyramid

13

Problem 1 Volume of Walter Pyramid

 Recall that the volume of a geometric solid is the amount of space contained inside the solid.

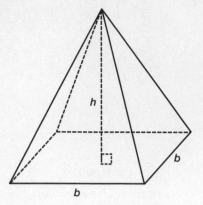

The volume, V, of a pyramid is determined by the formula $V = \frac{1}{3}b^2h$, where b represents the length and width of the square base, and h represents the height of the pyramid.

1. The diagram shown represents Walter Pyramid. Calculate the volume of Walter Pyramid. Show all of your work.

Walter Pyramid

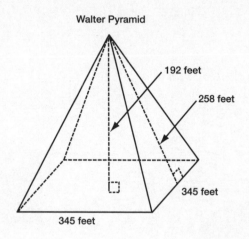

192 feet

258 feet

345 feet

345 feet

Wow, about how many football fields could you line up end-to-end and side-by-side in this arena?

13

Recall that the surface area of a geometric solid is the total area of the outside surfaces of the solid.

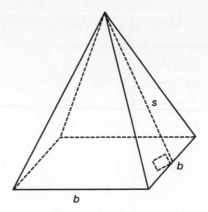

The five sides of the square pyramid are shown separately.

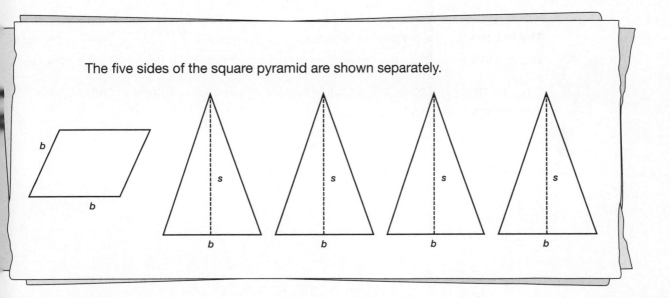

Since $b^2 + 4\left(\frac{1}{2}bs\right)$, then the surface area is $2bs + b^2$, the surface area, *SA*, of a square pyramid is determined by the formula $SA = 2bs + b^2$, where *b* represents the length/width of the square base of the pyramid and the length of the base of the triangular faces, and *s* represents the slant height of the pyramid and the height of the triangular faces of the pyramid.

How is the area of each surface represented in the first expression?

13

2. The diagram shown represents Walter Pyramid.

Calculate the surface area of Walter Pyramid. Show all of your work.

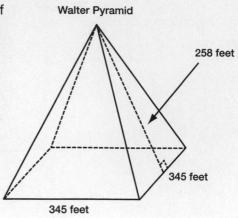

Walter Pyramid

258 feet

345 feet

345 feet

The diagram shown represents Pyramid Arena.

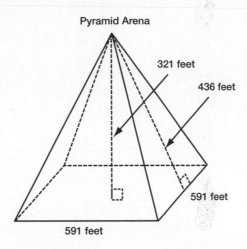

Pyramid Arena

321 feet

436 feet

591 feet

591 feet

1. Calculate the volume of Pyramid Arena.

Remember to show all of your work.

2. Calculate the surface area of Pyramid Arena.

13

Be prepared to share your solutions and methods.

13

13.1   Sketching, Modeling, and Describing the Cross-Sections of a Cube

A cross-section of a solid is the two-dimensional figure formed by the intersection of a plane and a solid when a plane passes through the solid.

Example

This trapezoid is the cross-section of a cube when it is cut by a plane as shown.

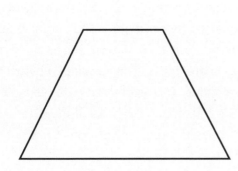 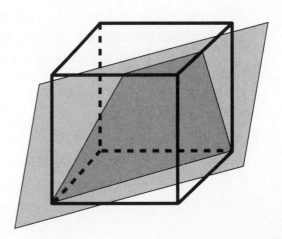

13

13.2 Sketching, Modeling, and Describing the Cross-Sections of a Right Rectangular Prism

A prism is a geometric solid that has parallel and congruent polygonal bases and lateral sides that are parallelograms. The types of cross-sections of a rectangular prism (that is not a cube) are similar to the types of cross-sections of a cube.

Example

The rectangle is the cross-section of the right rectangular prism when it is cut by a plane as shown.

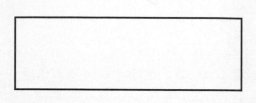
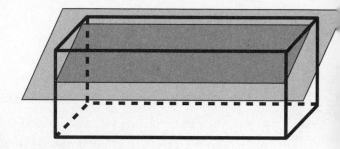

13.3 Sketching, Modeling, and Describing the Cross-Sections of a Right Rectangular Pyramid

A pyramid is a polyhedron formed by connecting one polygonal face to several triangular faces. The base of a pyramid is a single polygonal face. Similar to prisms, pyramids are classified by their bases. The triangular faces of a pyramid are called lateral faces. All lateral faces of a pyramid intersect at a common point. The lateral edges of a pyramid are the edges formed by the intersection of two lateral faces. The vertex of a pyramid is the point formed by the intersection of all lateral faces. The height of a pyramid is the perpendicular distance from the vertex of the pyramid to the base of the pyramid.
A regular pyramid is a pyramid in which the base is a regular polygon. The slant height of regular pyramid is the altitude of a lateral face.

13

Example

The trapezoid is the cross-section of the right rectangular pyramid when it is cut by a plane as shown.

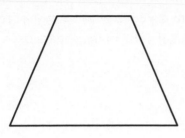

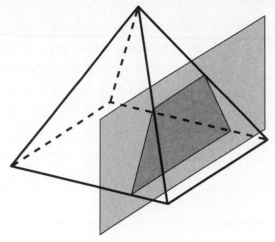

3.4 Exploring the Volume and Surface Area of a Solid

The volume of a solid three-dimensional object is the amount of space contained inside the object. Volume is described using cubic units of measure. The surface area of a solid three-dimensional object is the total area of the outside surfaces of the solid. Surface area is described using square units of measure. The volume, V, of a right rectangular prism is determined by the formula $V = l \times w \times h$, where l represents the length, w represents the width, and h represents the height of the prism. The surface area, SA, of a right rectangular prism is determined by the formula $SA = 2lw + 2lh + 2wh$.

Example

The right rectangular prism shown has a length of 8 feet, a width of 2 feet, and a height of 3 feet.

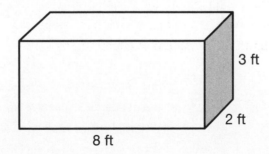

The volume of the prism is $V = 8 \times 2 \times 3 = 48$ cubic feet.

The surface area of the prism is
$SA = 2(8)(2) + 2(8)(3) + 2(2)(3) = 32 + 48 + 12 = 92$ square feet.

13.5 Exploring the Volume and Surface Area of Pyramids

The volume, V, of a square pyramid is determined by the formula $V = \frac{1}{3}b^2h$, where b represents the length and width of the square base, and h represents the height of the pyramid. The surface area, SA, of a square pyramid is determined by the formula $SA = 2bs + b^2$, where b represents the length and width of the square base, and s represents the slant height of the pyramid.

Example

A pyramid has a square base with a length and width of 12 meters. The height of the pyramid is 16 meters, and the slant height of the pyramid is 20 meters.

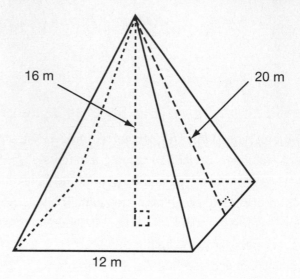

16 m   20 m

12 m

The volume of the pyramid is $V = \frac{1}{3}(12)^2\,(16) = \frac{1}{3}(144)(16) = 48(16) = 768$ cubic meters.

The surface area of the pyramid is
$SA = 2(12)(20) + (12)^2 = 480 + 144 = 624$ square meters.

> Did you know the Egyptians were some of the first mathematicians? They drew blueprints before creating the pyramids, developed a number system in hieroglyphics, and even kept their brains sharp with math puzzles!

14 DATA COLLECTION

The iGeneration—people born in the 1990's and 2000's—are the most wired people in the United States. By some estimates, iGeners spend as much as ⊃ hours a day using technology and media. This is possible because they do several tasks, such as texting and surfing the web, at the same time.

14

WE WANT TO HEAR FROM YOU!

Formulating Questions and Collecting Data

Learning Goals

In this lesson, you will:

▶ Collect data from a survey and analyze the results.

▶ Differentiate between a census and a sample.

▶ Differentiate between a parameter and a statistic.

Key Terms

▶ survey
▶ data
▶ population
▶ census
▶ sample
▶ parameter
▶ statistic

"Text your vote for who should stay on the show!"

"Will the Tigers defensive line be able to stop run plays?"

"Why do you think the president's approval rating is rising?"

These and many other questions are posed to people on a daily basis. Sports, news, and entertainment television shows ask viewers to call in, email, or text opinions.

Media companies have always wanted the opinions of their viewers. With the progress of computer technology and cell phone communication, getting those opinions has become easier to get. It has also become easier to report the results associated with such opinions. Have you ever been asked to take a survey? Did you ever wonder how people are chosen to take a survey, or why a survey is conducted?

14

Problem 1 Taking a Survey

 A **survey** is a method of collecting information about a certain group of people. It involv asking a question or a set of questions to those people. When information is collected, facts or numbers gathered are called **data**.

How could you describe the students in your classroom? How do the students in your classroom compare to other groups of students in your school, or to other seventh graders in the United States?

1. Answer each question in the survey shown.

7th Grade Math Class Survey

Teacher: _____

Class period or time: _____

1. What is your approximate height in inches?

   _____

2. What color is your hair?

   Brown___   Blond___   Black___   Red___   Other___

3. Do you carry a cell phone with you?

   Yes___   No___

4. About how many text messages do you send in one day?

   _____

5. About how much time (in minutes) do you spend doing homework each week?

   _____

6. What is your favorite type of TV show to watch?

   Comedy___   Sports___   Reality___   Drama___

   Educational___   News___   Music___   Other___

14

The **population** is the entire set of items from which data can be selected. When you decide what you want to study, the population is the set of all elements in which you are interested. The elements of that population can be people or objects.

Some examples of populations include:

- every person in the United States
- every person in your math class
- every person in your school
- all the apples in your supermarket
- all the apples in the world

A **census** is the data collected from every member of a population.

1. Use your survey to answer each question.

   a. Besides you, who else took the math class survey?

   b. What is the population in your class survey?

   c. Are the data collected in the class survey a census? Explain your reasoning.

Ever since 1790, the United States has taken a census every 10 years to collect data about population and state resources. The original purposes of the census were to decide the number of representatives a state could send to the U.S. House of Representatives, and to determine the federal tax burden.

Did you know, according to the 2010 census, approximately 309,000,000 people live in the United States?

2. Describe the population for the United States census?

14

3. Why do you think this collection of data is called "the census"?

In most cases, it is not possible or logical to collect data from every member of the population. When data are collected from a part of the population, the data is called a **sample**. A sample should be representative of the population. In other words, it should have characteristics that are similar to the entire population.

When data are gathered from a population, the characteristic used to describe the population is called a **parameter**.

When data are gathered from a sample, the characteristic used to describe the sample is called a **statistic**. A statistic is used to make an estimate about the parameter.

4. After the 2000 census, the United States Census Bureau reported that 7.4% of Georgia residents were between the ages of 10 and 14.
   Was a parameter or a statistic reported? Explain your reasoning.

5. A recent survey of 1000 teenagers from across the United States shows that 4 out of 5 carry a cell phone with them.

   a. What is the population in the survey?

   b. Were the data collected in the survey a census? Why or why not?

   c. Does the given statement represent a parameter or a statistic? Explain how you determined your answer.

   d. Of those 1000 teenagers surveyed, how many carry a cell phone? How many do not carry a cell phone?

6. Use the survey you completed in Problem 1, or the data provided at the end of this lesson to answer each question.

    a. How many students in the class carry a cell phone with them? Use a complete sentence in your answer.

    b. What percent of the students in the class carry a cell phone with them? Use a complete sentence in your answer.

    c. Does the percent of students in the class that carry a cell phone represent a parameter or a statistic? Explain how you determined your answer.

7. Possible samples to determine the number of students who carry a cell phone with them are provided. Discuss whether or not the samples represent all students in a class. Use complete sentences to justify your answers.

   a. the selection of all of the girls for the sample

   b. the selection of the students in the first seat of every row

   c. the selection of every fourth student alphabetically

Oh, I see! To get accurate characteristics of a population, I must carefully select a sample that represents the population.

   d. the selection of the first 10 students to enter the classroom

14

1. Describe the relationship between a population and a sample.

2. What do you think it means to say that a sample must be representative of the population?

3. What is the purpose of a statistic?

Be prepared to share your solutions and methods.

14

Results from Class Survey						
Student	1. What is your approximate height?	2. What color is your hair?	3. Do you carry a cell phone with you?	4. About how many text messages do you send in one day?	5. About how much time do you spend doing homework each week?	6. What is your favorite type of show to watch?
1-Sue (F)	60 in.	Red	Yes	75	120 minutes	Reality
2-Jorge (M)	68 in.	Brown	Yes	5	60 minutes	Sports
3-Alex (M)	63 in.	Brown	No	0	100 minutes	Music
4-Maria (F)	65 in.	Blond	Yes	20	100 minutes	Comedy
5-Tamika (F)	62 in.	Brown	Yes	50	150 minutes	Comedy
6-Sarah (F)	68 in.	Black	Yes	100	10 minutes	Drama
7-Beth (F)	56 in.	Blond	Yes	60	45 minutes	Reality
8-Sam (M)	70 in.	Black	No	0	300 minutes	Sports
9-Eric (M)	69 in.	Other	Yes	50	60 minutes	Sports
0-Marcus (M)	66 in.	Red	Yes	100	50 minutes	Reality
11-Carla (F)	61 in.	Brown	Yes	0	150 minutes	Music
12-Ben (M)	68 in.	Blond	Yes	60	60 minutes	Reality
13-Will (M)	64 in.	Brown	Yes	50	120 minutes	Comedy
14-Yasmin (F)	66 in.	Brown	Yes	40	150 minutes	Drama
15-Paulos (M)	60 in.	Brown	Yes	90	30 minutes	Reality
16-Jon (M)	67 in.	Blond	Yes	10	150 minutes	Music
17-Rose (F)	64 in.	Brown	Yes	0	200 minutes	Other
18-Donna (F)	65 in.	Brown	Yes	25	90 minutes	Sports
19-Suzi (F)	63 in.	Black	Yes	30	90 minutes	Reality
20-Kayla (F)	58 in.	Blond	Yes	80	200 minutes	Reality

14

14

14.2

DEALING WITH DATA: SELECTING A SAMPLE

Collecting Data through Random Sampling

Learning Goals

In this lesson, you will:

▶ Differentiate between a random sample and a sample that is not chosen randomly.

▶ Use several methods to select a random sample.

Key Terms

▶ random sample
▶ random number generator
▶ random number table

When was the last time your school got new lunch tables or lockers? Or when was the last time your school purchased new language arts or science books? Or how often does your classroom get cleaned? All of these are expenses that schools pay for—some on a weekly or monthly basis, while others may occur every three to five years. But how much do these expenses amount to per student?

Studies have shown that it can cost a state roughly between $5000 and $10,000 per year to educate students. In fact, in the 2007-2008 school year, New York spent roughly $17,000 per student in public schools! So, how much do you think your school pays to educate you per year?

14

Problem 1 Selecting a Sample

Wellington Middle School decides to place small storage lockers in every classroom for students to use. The lockers will be mounted on the walls at student eye level. To determine how far above the floor the lockers should be mounted, Ms. Genier, the school principal, needs to calculate the mean height of students in the school. Because there is not enough time to measure the height of every student at the school, Ms. Genier decides to survey 25 students from the school to measure their heights. She will then calculate the mean height to help her determine how high to mount the lockers.

1. What is the population for Ms. Genier's survey?

2. What is the sample?

3. If Ms. Genier calculates the mean height of the 25 students, will the result represent parameter or a statistic? Explain your reasoning.

4. Analyze each way Ms. Genier could take a sample. Then, determine if any or all the samples could inaccurately represent the mean height of the entire school. Explain your reasoning for each.

   a. Ms. Genier selects the first 25 students to arrive at school.

14

b. Ms. Genier chooses 25 students in one of the 6th grade math classes.

c. Ms. Genier selects 25 students from the soccer team.

d. Ms. Genier gives each student a raffle ticket with a number. Then, she selects 25 numbers by drawing them from a hat.

When information is collected from a sample in order to describe a characteristic about the population, it is important that such a sample be as representative of the population as possible. A **random sample** is a sample that is selected from the population in such a way that every member of the population has the same chance of being selected.

14

Problem 2 Choosing a Random Sample

Ms. Levi is purchasing a variety of posters to hang in her classroom. She wants to hang the posters at student eye level and decides to use the mean height of students in her math class as a guide. Rather than using the heights of all students in her class, she decides to take a random sample of students in her class.

1. What is the population for this problem?

2. Ms. Levi received two suggestions to randomly sample her class. Decide if each strategy represents a random sample. If not, explain why not.

   a. Ms. Levi chooses the girls in the class.

   b. Ms. Levi chooses all the students wearing white sneakers.

3. Ms. Levi decides to select a random sample of five students in her class, and then calculate the mean height. She assigns each student in her class a different number. Then, she randomly selects 5 numbers.

a. Explain why Ms. Levi's method of taking a sample is a random sample.

b. Do you think randomly selecting 5 students will accurately represent the population of her class? If not, do you think she should pick more or less students?

c. Damien hopes Ms. Levi will assign him the number 7 because it will have a better chance of being selected for the sample. Do you agree or disagree with Damien? Explain your reasoning.

d. Julie claims Ms. Levi must begin with the number 1 when assigning numbers to students. Jorge says she can start with any number as long as she assigns every student a different number. Who is correct? Explain.

When choosing a random sample from a population that has many members, it would take a long time to assign each number to each student, write each assigned number or slip of paper, and then draw numbers to choose a random sample.

There are other ways to select a random sample. One way to select a random sample involves using a *random number generator*. A **random number generator** is any computer program or calculator that can generate numbers such that each number has equal chance of occurring each time.

4. Let's use a graphing calculator to help Ms. Levi randomly select five students from her class.

   a. Ms. Levi has assigned each of her 30 students a different number starting with the number 1. Follow the graphing calculator steps to randomly generate 5 numbers.

      Step 1: Press MATH to access the Math menu on your graphing calculator. Then, use the right arrow to highlight PRB .

      Step 2: Use the down arrow to highlight **5: randInt (** and press ENTER .

      ```
      MATH NUM CPX PRB
      1:rand
      2:npr
      3:ncr
      4:!
      5:randInt(
      6:randNorm(
      7:randBin(
      ```

      Step 3: Enter 1, 30) and press ENTER .

      A number from 1 through 30 should appear.

      Step 4: Press ENTER 4 more times to get a sample of 5 random numbers.

   b. Record the 5 numbers your graphing calculator generated.

   c. Compare your sample with the samples of your classmates. What do you notice?

14

5. Ms. Levi had previously assigned each of the 30 students in her class a different number, starting with 15. How could you change Step 3 of the graphing calculator instructions to accommodate the list beginning at 15?

6. Suppose that the 5 numbers generated on the graphing calculator resulted in 5 girls.

   a. Does that mean the sample is not a random sample? Explain your reasoning.

   b. How is this outcome different from the outcome of Question 1, part (b) where Ms. Levi decided to select all girls to represent her sample?

14

Problem 3   Using Random Number Tables

Random number tables are tables that can contain hundreds of digits. They usually displ
the numbers with a space after every five digits so that the digits are easier to read. Some
tables also place a space after every five lines for the same reason.

Use the random number table shown to answer Questions 1 through 7. The complete
table is at the end of this lesson.

Line 4	12645	62000	61555	76404	86210	11808	12841	45147	97438	6002
Line 5	78137	98768	24689	87130	71223	08151	84963	64539	79493	7491

Line 6	62490	99215	84987	28759	19177	14733	24550	28067	68894	3849
Line 7	24216	63444	21283	07044	92729	37284	13211	37485	10415	3645

1. Beginning on Line 6, write the first eight random digits.

2. Why do you think the digit 9 occurred multiple times, and the digit 3 did not
   occur at all?

You can also use a random number table to choose a number that has any number of
digits in it. For example, if you are choosing 6 three-digit random numbers and begin with
Line 7, the first 6 three-digit random numbers would be: 242, 166, 344, 421, 283, and 070

3. What number does "070" represent when choosing a three-digit random number?
   Why are the zeros in the number included? Explain your reasoning.

4. If selecting a three-digit random number, how would the number 5 be displayed in the table?

5. Begin on Line 4 and select 5 three-digit random numbers.

6. Explain how to assign numbers to 100 people so that you can take a random sample.

7. Ms. Levi decides to use the random number table to select 5 students for a random sample. She begins on Line 5 and assigns each of her 30 students a two-digit number beginning with 1.

  a. How would the random number for student 7 appear in the table?

  b. What is the first number that appears?

  c. What do you think Ms. Levi should do with that number?

d. Continuing on Line 5, what are the 5 two-digit numbers to be used to select Ms. Levi's sample?

e. Begin on Line 7 and choose 5 two-digit numbers for Ms. Levi's sample. Who are the students chosen for the sample?

f. What should you do if a two-digit number appears twice in the random number table?

Oh oh! What should I do if a number is repeated when I am choosing from a random number table? Should use the number the first tim it comes up? Or the second tim Or should I not use that number?

g. Will choosing a line number affect if Ms. Levi's sample is random?

h. Will choosing a line number affect who will be chosen for the sample?

14

1. There are 2500 students in Jackson Middle School. The principal wishes to select a random sample of 10 students to have lunch with, and discuss ways to improve school spirit.

a. What is the population for this problem?

b. What is the sample for this problem?

c. How would you recommend the principal assign the random numbers?

14

2. The coach of the soccer team is asked to select 5 students to represent the team in the Homecoming Parade. The coach decides to randomly select the 5 students out the 38 members of the team.

a. What is the population for this problem?

b. What is the sample for this problem?

c. How would you recommend the coach assign the random numbers?

 Be prepared to share your solutions and methods.

14

14.3

FLOOR PLANS AND TILES

Random Sampling

Learning Goals

In this lesson, you will:

▶ Investigate how results from a random sample are more reliable in representing the population than results from a sample that is not random.

▶ Use sampling and proportional reasoning to predict the value of a population parameter.

Key Term

▶ dot plot (line plot)

Have you ever heard of the word "mosaic"? This art form has been used to create landscapes, and images of political and religious figures. Mosaics have also been used to add colors and patterns to floors, ceilings, and courtyards. Originally, mosaics were completed by hand. However, more mosaics are being created by robotics that can design and assemble mosaics in a quicker amount of time and with more accuracy. What do you think a mosaic is?

14

Problem 1 Selecting Squares

The Art Club created a design on the floor of the art room. Each of the 40 numbered squares on the floor will have colored tiles. The club needs to calculate how many tiles they must buy. Each small grid square represents a square that is one foot long and one foot wide.

							#9				#10		#12		#13
#1															
#2		#3		#4			#8			#11					
												#15		#14
	#5	#7							#16				
#6	#18				#17						
	#19	#20	#22		#21				
#24	#25	#26		#23			
		#27				
#38	#28	#30	#32
#39	#29	#31	#33
#37		#34
#40	#36	#35	

1. How can the Art Club members calculate the amount of tiles they will need?

The Art Club needs to complete the art room floor plan project by tomorrow! Because they are short of time, they decide they do not have enough time to measure all 40 squares. Samantha says, "Since we don't have a lot of time, why don't we just select 5 squares and calculate their total area. That should be good enough for us to estimate the total area of all the squares that will need tiles."

2. Do you think Samantha's idea could work to estimate the total area for all the squares that need tiles? Explain your reasoning.

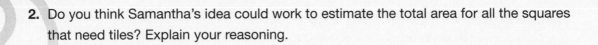

Samantha's idea of taking a sample of 5 squares can work to estimate the total area of the 40 squares in the design floor plan.

As you learned, you can select a sample to determine parameters of a population. In this problem situation, the art club is going to set up a ratio using the sample of squares they select to the total area of those sample squares.

They will use the ratio:

number of squares in the sample : total area of the sample squares.

Samantha decides to select the following squares: 1, 15, 21, 37, and 40.

Total area

Square 1: 1 × 1 = 1 square unit

Square 15: 2 × 2 = 4 square units

Square 21: 7 × 7 = 49 square units

Square 37: 4 × 4 = 16 square units

Square 40: 2 × 2 = 4 square units

Ratio

number of squares in the sample : total area of the sample squares
5 squares : 74 square units

So, the total area of these 5 squares is 74 square units.

Use the Art Club members' floor plan to answer Questions 3 through 7.

3. What is the population for this problem?

14

4. Select 5 numbered squares that you think best represent the 40 squares to be painted. Record the numbers of the squares you selected.

5. Calculate the total area of the 5 numbered squares you selected.

6. Is the total area of the 5 numbered squares a parameter or a statistic? Explain your reasoning.

Previously, you learned about three common distributions of data: skewed left, skewed right, and symmetric. You have also learned that the distribution of data can help you determine whether the mean or median is a better measure of center. Let's look at the diagrams shown.

Skewed Right	**Symmetric**	**Skewed Left**
A graph or a plot that is skewed right has much of its data to the left with only a few data values being plotted to the right.	A symmetric graph typically has a high point or peak in the middle of the data set. The data points on the left and right side of the peak are mirror images of each other.	A graph or a plot that is skewed left has much of its data to the right with only a few data values being plotted to the left.

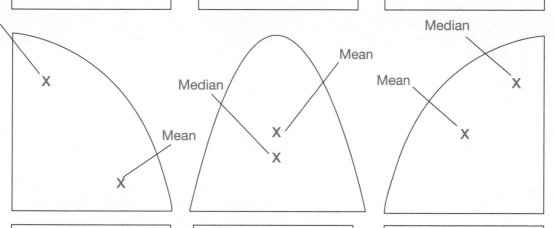

| The mean of a data set is greater than the median when the data is skewed to the right.

The median is the best measure of center because the median is not affected by very small data values. | The mean and median are or about equal when the data is symmetric.

The mean is the best measure of center. | The mean of a data set is less than the median when the data is skewed to the left.

The median is the best measure of center. |
|---|---|---|

The median is not affected by very large or very small data values.

14

7. Compare the total area of your sample to the total areas your classmates' samples.

  a. Record the total area you calculated for your sample on the dot plot shown. Ther record the total areas your classmates calculated on the same dot plot.

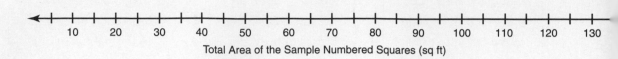

Total Area of the Sample Numbered Squares (sq ft)

  b. Describe the distribution of the dot plot.

  c. Estimate the total area for a sample of 5 squares using the data values in the dot plot

8. When you chose your sample, was it a random sample? Explain your reasoning.

Now that you have set up a ratio of the sample of 5 squares to the total area of those 5 sample squares, you can set up a proportion to estimate the total area of those 40 squares in the art club's design floor plan. In doing so, you are scaling up from your sample to the population of the squares.

9. Estimate the total area of all 40 squares on the floor plan using proportional reasoning.

10. Compare the estimated total area of the 40 squares on the floor plan with your classmates' estimated total areas.

   a. Record the estimated total area of the 40 squares on the floor plan you estimated using proportional reasoning on the dot plot shown. Then, record your classmates' estimates of the total area of the 40 squares.

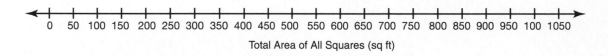

0   50 100 150 200 250 300 350 400 450 500 550 600 650 700 750 800 850 900 950 100 1050

Total Area of All Squares (sq ft)

11. Estimate the total area of the squares in the floor plan using data values in the dot plot.

Problem 2 Selecting Squares Randomly

 Samples chosen by looking at the squares and trying to pick certain squares will probabl contain many more of the larger squares in the floor plan. Most of the squares actually have small areas (17 of the 40 squares have an area of 1 square foot, and 10 of the 40 squares have an area of 4 square feet); therefore, you need to use another method to randomly choose squares.

1. How might you randomly choose 5 squares for your sample?

2. Soo Jin has a suggestion on how to randomly select the numbered squares. She says, "I can cut out the squares from the floor plan, and then I can put these squares in a bag. That will help me randomly select squares." Will Soo Jin's method result in a random sample? Explain your reasoning or suggest a way to modify her strategy.

3. How can you use the random number table to choose 5 numbered squares for your sample?

Patrice begins on Line 12 of the random number table to choose her random sample of 5 numbered squares.

Line 11	96155	95009	27429	72918	08457	78134	48407	26061	58754	05326
Line 12	29621	66583	62966	12468	20245	14015	04014	35713	03980	03024
Line 13	12639	75291	71020	17265	41598	64074	64629	63293	53307	48766
Line 14	14544	37134	54714	02401	63228	26831	19386	15457	17999	18306
Line 15	83403	88827	09834	11333	68431	31706	26652	04711	34593	22561

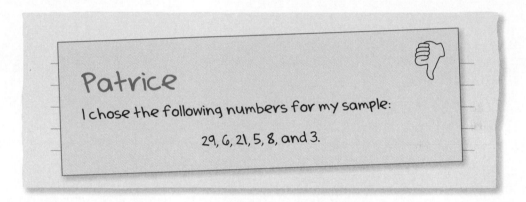

Patrice

I chose the following numbers for my sample:

29, 6, 21, 5, 8, and 3.

4. Explain why Patrice did not correctly select the correct numbers for a random sample.

14

5. Use the random number table from Question 4. Begin on any line except Line 12 an choose 5 numbered squares using two-digit numbers ranging between 01 and 40. Record the square numbers.

6. Calculate the total area of the 5 numbered squares you selected.

7. Compare the total area of your sample to the total areas your classmates calculated through their samples.

a. Record the total areas your classmates calculated and the total area you calculated on the dot plot shown.

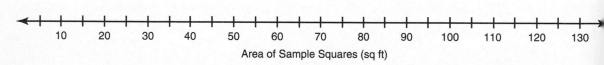

Area of Sample Squares (sq ft)

b. How do the values plotted on this dot plot compare to the values plotted in Problem 1, Question 7? Compare the shapes and the centers of the data values for both dot plots.

14

8. Estimate the total area of all 40 squares on the floor plan using the area you calculated from the random sample and proportional reasoning.

9. Compare your estimated total area from the random sample for all 40 squares with your classmates' total area estimates.

a. Record your estimated total area of the 40 squares on the dot plot shown. Then, record your classmates' estimates of the total area of the 40 squares on the dot plot.

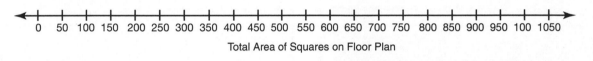

Total Area of Squares on Floor Plan

b. Estimate the total area of the squares in the floor plan using data values in the dot plot.

10. How do the values plotted on this dot plot compare to the values plotted in Problem 1, Question 10? Compare the distributions and the centers of the data values for both dot plots.

14

11. The actual total area of the 40 numbered squares is 288 square feet. Is 288 a parameter or a statistic? Explain your reasoning.

12. Locate 288 on each line plot you created. What do you notice?

Talk the Talk

1. What is the purpose of taking a sample?

2. What conclusions can you make about estimating a parameter from a statistic that is calculated from a random sample when compared to a statistic calculated from a sample that is not random?

Be prepared to share your solutions and methods.

WHAT DOES THE DATA MEAN?

Using Samples, Centers, and Spreads to Describe Data

Learning Goals

In this lesson, you will:

▶ Analyze measures of center for samples from a population.

▶ Analyze measures of variation for samples from a population.

Key Terms

▶ variability

▶ spread

▶ range

▶ mean absolute deviation

▶ deviation from the mean

Do you think your brain is a muscle? In actuality, the brain is not a muscle, but many experts suggest that regular "brain workouts" keep the brain sharp. Experts suggest that solving crossword puzzles, Sudoku puzzles, reading, even regularly studying for tests are examples of exercising the brain. Experts also believe that keeping the brain active can possibly help in the prevention of Alzheimer's (pronounced alz-hy–mers) disease. So, what brain activities do you participate in? Do you think playing video games is a good brain workout?

14

Problem 1   Time to Hit the Books!

Previously, you were asked to estimate the number of minutes you spend studying each week. For the School Board report, your principal asks every math teacher in Allentown Middle School to estimate the amount of time their students spend studying each week.

1. Allentown's math teacher decides to take a sample of 8 students in her math class. Then, she can determine the mean amount of time students spend studying each week.

   a. What is the population?

   b. What is the sample that Allentown's Middle School will use to estimate the average amount of time students will study?

   c. Describe the parameter and the statistic for this problem.

Maria selects a random sample of 8 students. She uses Line 1 of the random number table at the back of the lesson to select 8 students.

The students Maria selects are student numbers 12, 13, 10, 11, 16, 14, 4, and 20.

The minutes these students spent studying are 60, 120, 50, 150, 150, 50, 100, and 200.

She then writes the number of minutes each student spent studying in the table shown.

Finally, she determined the mean number of minutes these 8 students spend studying is 110 minutes.

ple ber	Student Number	Minutes Spent Studying Each Week	Mean Number of Minutes Spent Studying Each Week	Mean Absolute Deviation of Minutes Spent Studying Each Week
	12	60		
	13	120		
	10	50		
	11	150	$\frac{880}{8} = 110$ min.	
	16	150		
	14	50		
	04	100		
	20	200		

2. How did Maria determine the mean number of minutes the students spent studying?

3. Take 4 more samples of 8 students. Use the data at the end of the lesson, and use the random number table at the end of the chapter to gather your information. You can use any line in the random number table except for Line 1. Record your results in the table in the first three columns of the table. Then, determine the mean for each sample.

For the time being, ignore the last olumn in the table—we will explore that column later in the lesson!

It's okay if a student appears in more than one sample. Just remember that the same student can *not* appear more than once in *one* sample.

14

Sample Number	Student Number	Minutes Spent Studying Each Week	Mean Number of Minutes Spent Studying Each Week	Mean Absolute Deviation of Minutes Spent Studying Each Week
1	12	60	$\frac{880}{8} = 110$ min.	$60-110 = -50 \quad |-50| = 50$
	13	120		$120-110 = 10 \quad |10| = 10$
	10	50		$50-110 = -60 \quad |-60| = 60$
	11	150		$150-110 = 40 \quad |40| = 40$
	16	150		$150-110 = 40 \quad |40| = 40$
	14	50		$50-110 = -60 \quad |-60| = 60$
	04	100		$100-110 = -10 \quad |-10| = 10$
	20	200		$200-110 = 90 \quad |90| = 90$
				$\frac{50 + 10 + 60 + 40 + 40 + 60 + 10 + 90}{8} = \frac{360}{8} =$
2				

14

...ple ...ber	Student Number	Minutes Spent Studying Each Week	Mean Number of Minutes Spent Studying Each Week	Mean Absolute Deviation of Minutes Spent Studying Each Week

Sample Number	Student Number	Minutes Spent Studying Each Week	Mean Number of Minutes Spent Studying Each Week	Mean Absolute Deviation of Minutes Spent Studying Each Week
5				

4. What do you notice about the mean of each sample?

5. Plot the sample means on a number line. Then, use the results to estimate the mean number of minutes spent studying each week from the samples.

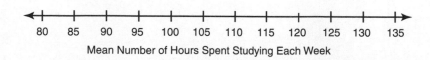

Mean Number of Hours Spent Studying Each Week

6. Calculate the mean number of minutes students spent studying each week from the 5 means of the random samples. Compare your answer to your estimate in Question 5. What do you notice?

As you can see, there can be quite a difference in the means when selecting multiple samples. The distribution of this data is sometimes called the *variability* of data. The **variability** of data describes how "spread out" the data is. This can also be described as the **spread** of data.

One of the simplest measures of variability or spread is the *range* of data. The **range** of data refers to the minimum and maximum values in a data set. So, in Maria's sample, the range of data was a minimum of 50 minutes and a maximum of 200 minutes.

Another spread of data is analyzing the difference means from multiple random samples.

Although the individual means of the random samples vary, analyzing the means for several random samples provides a good estimate for the mean of a population. By analyzing the means of multiple random samples, you can determine the *mean absolute deviation*. The **mean absolute deviation** is the average of the absolute values of the deviations of each data value from the mean. Remember, the absolute value of a number is the distance the number is from zero on a number line.

The mean absolute deviation is calculated by performing the following steps:

- Subtract the mean from each data value in a sample. This is called the **deviation from the mean.**
- Determine the absolute value of each deviation.
- Calculate the mean of the absolute values of the deviation.

7. Calculate the mean absolute deviation for each sample in Problem 1. Record your calculations in the table.

8. Analyze the mean absolute deviation for each sample. What do you notice?

9. Plot the mean absolute deviations on a number line.

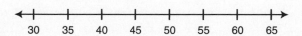

14

10. Describe the range of the mean absolute deviations.

11. If you calculated the mean absolute deviation for the entire class, do you think that this would be less than, greater than, or equal to the mean?

If you were to calculate the mean absolute deviation of all of the students (the population) it would be greater than the mean absolute deviations of each sample. For example, the mean absolute deviation of the entire Allentown Middle School math class is 74.425, which is greater than the mean absolute deviation of each sample. This is because the population data values' variability is almost always greater than a sample's variability. Also, remember that the mean is affected by extreme minimum and maximum values.

Problem 2   I Can Summarize Data in Five Numbers!

Let's analyze data sets and variability in another way. The five number summary is one way to analyze a data set. Remember, the five number summary consists of the:

- Minimum, which is the least data value in the entire data set,
- First Quartile (Q1), which is the median for the data values between the minimum and the median of the entire data set,
- Median, which is the number in the middle of the entire data set,
- Third Quartile (Q3), which is the median for the data values between the median of the entire data set and the maximum data value,
- Maximum, which is the greatest data value in the entire data set.

Also, recall that the Interquartile Range (IQR) is the difference between Q3 and Q1. The IQR is another measure of variability, or spread of a data set.

14

For example, you can calculate the five number summary for the first sample of the Allentown Middle School math class. The data values are shown.

60 120 50 150 150 50 100 200

Step 1: Determine the minimum and maximum.
The minimum is 50 and the maximum is 200.

Step 2: Determine the median of the data set.
It is more efficient to write the data set in ascending order.

50 50 60 100 120 150 150 200

Because there are an even number of data points, you need to determine the mean of the two middle numbers.

$$\frac{100 + 120}{2} = 110$$

Step 3: Now that you have determined the median, write the data values less than the median in ascending order to determine Q1.

50 50 60 100

Once again, you need to calculate the mean of the two middle numbers of the data in the lower quartile.

$$\frac{50 + 60}{2} = 55$$

You need to follow the same process to calculate Q3. Write the data values greater than the median in ascending order to determine Q3.

120 150 150 200

The median of $\frac{150 + 150}{2} = 150$

14

The five number summary for the first sample of the Allentown Middle School math class is written in the table shown.

1. Determine the five number summary and the IQR for the second sample you conducted. Record your calculations in the table shown.

Sample	Minimum	Q1	Median	Q3	Maximum	IQR
1	50	55	110	150	200	150−55 = 95
2						
3						
4						
5						

Can you think of another way to determine a five number summary?

14

Using a Graphing Calculator to Determine Five Number Summaries

You can use a graphing calculator to determine the five number summary of a data set. You will determine the five number summary for the second sample of the Allentown Middle School math class' study time.

Step 1: Press [STAT] and **EDIT 1: Edit** should be highlighted. Then, press [ENTER].

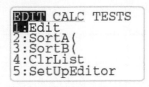

Step 2: Enter the data set into L1. Unlike determining the mean and median on paper, it is *not* necessary to enter the data in numerical order. Press [ENTER] after you enter each data value.

200   120   90   150   60   90   150   100

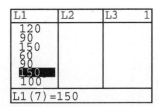

Step 3: Press [STAT] and scroll left to **CALC** . The **1: 1-Var Stats** should be highlighted. Press [ENTER]. The screen should display **1-Var Stats.**

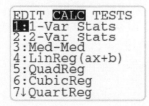
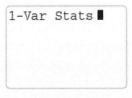

14

The default setting is **List 1 (L1),** so you can press ENTER . You should get the screen shown.

```
1-Var Stats
  x̄=120
  Σx=960
  Σx2=129200
  Sx=44.72135955
  σx=41.83300133
 ↓n=8
```

The screen shown displays a variety of statistics about the data. The x̄ represents the mean of the data set. The mean number of minutes the students studies was 120 minute The n = 8 indicates that there are 8 values in the list.

The down arrow, ↓, indicates there is additional information. Press ↓ until the median is displayed. Median on the graphing calculator is shown as Med =.

After you scroll down, you will see the five number summary displayed for the second sample. The minX represents the minimum data value. The maxX represents the maximu data value. Q1 is displayed after the minimum data value. Q3 is displayed just before the maximum data value.

```
1-Var Stats
 ↑n=15
  minX=0
  Q1=20
  Med=40
  Q3=60
  maxX=300
```

The median number of minutes the students studied in the second sample is 110 minute

1. What do you notice about the five number summary shown on your graphing calculator and the five number summary you wrote in the table for Problem 2.

2. Use your graphing calculator to determine the five number summary for the three remaining samples for the Allentown Middle School data. Then, write the five numbe summary in the table for Problem 2.

3. Calculate the IQR for each sample. Then, write each sample's IQR in the table for Problem 2.

14

4. Determine the five number summary and IQR for the class data for the entire Allentown Middle School math class using your graphing calculator.

MINIMUM:

Q1:

MEDIAN:

Q3:

MAXIMUM:

IQR:

5. What do you notice about the spreads of the 5 samples, and the spread of the population of the Allentown Middle School data set?

14

Problem 4 What Does a Five Number Summary Look Like?

A way to graphically display a five number summary is to construct a box-and-whisker plot.

To make a box-and-whisker plot for Sample 1, follow the steps shown.

First, draw a number line.

Next, place a vertical line above the median value of the data set.

Then, place vertical lines above the Q1 and Q3 values. Draw a rectangle, or a "box," with the vertical lines for Q1 and Q3 as the sides of the box.

Finally, place two dots above the minimum and maximum values above the number line. Connect the dots to the sides of the box to create the "whiskers."

Sample 1

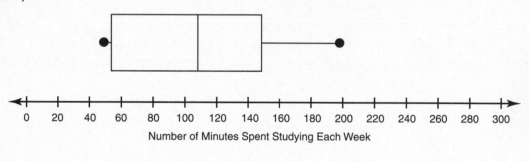

1. Construct a box-and-whisker plot for the second sample you conducted.

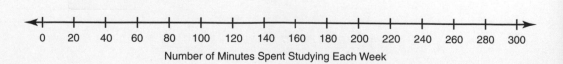

You can also use a graphing calculator to construct a box-and-whisker plot. Follow the graphing calculator steps shown to graph the study data for the third sample of the Allentown Middle School math class.

Let's begin by entering the data set into List 1 of the calculator.

Step 1: Press [STAT] . [EDIT] and [1:Edit] should be highlighted. Then, press [ENTER] .

Step 2: Enter the data into L1. If there are data values in **L1**, highlight **L1** and press [CLEAR] . It is *not* necessary to enter the data in numerical order. Press [ENTER] after you enter each data value.

90 300 60 150 60 200 120 100

```
L1        L2        L3      1
 300
 60
 150
 60
 200
 120
 100
L1(7)=120
```

Step 3: Construct the box-and-whisker plot.

Press [Y=] and delete any equations that have been entered. To delete an equation, use the [CLEAR] key.

You may also wish to turn off the axes by pressing [2nd] [ZOOM] , using the arrows to highlight **AxesOff** , and pressing [ENTER] .

Press [2nd] key followed by [Y=] key. Make sure that Plot 1 is On and the other Plots are Off. Press [ENTER] .

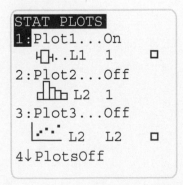

14

- Press [ENTER] on Plot 1, then scroll to On.
- Use the arrow keys to highlight the box-and-whisker plot and press [ENTER] (Note: The first box-and-whisker plot icon displays outliers.)
- Make certain Xlist: displays L1.
- There are two ways to have the calculator display the graph. Pressing [ZOOM] followed by [9] will result in the box-and-whisker plot being displayed. If you prefer to determine the range of data that will be displayed, you can press [WINDOW] and enter the values for **Xmin** and **Xmax**. Press [GRAPH].
- You can determine the values for the five-number summary by pressing [TRACE] and using the left and right arrows.

Your graphing calculator should display the box-and-whisker plot shown. To determine t values of the five number summary, use the [→] to scroll to each value.

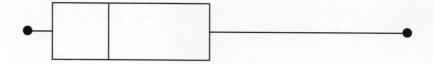

2. Use your graphing calculator to construct box-and-whisker plots for the remaining two samples for Allentown Middle School math class study times. Then, sketch each of the samples on the number lines shown.

a.

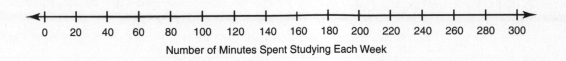

Number of Minutes Spent Studying Each Week

b.

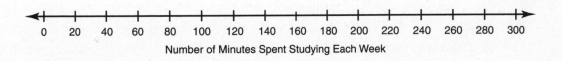

Number of Minutes Spent Studying Each Week

14

3. Construct a box-and-whiskers plot of the data from the entire Allentown Middle School math class using your graphing calculator. Then, compare the box plot to the box plots of the samples you sketched. What do you notice?

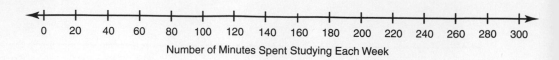

Number of Minutes Spent Studying Each Week

You used many different measures of variability, or spread of data to analyze data sets. Because the data set for the Allentown Middle School only consisted of 20 data points, you could calculate the measures of center more efficiently than calculating the mean absolute deviation or the interquartile range. For large data sets when it is difficult or impossible to calculate a parameter such as the mean or median, means, medians, mean absolute deviation, and interquartile range of several random samples can provide good estimates of the population mean.

14

1. What are the advantages to calculating the mean absolute deviation or interquartile range from multiple samples for a population that consists of many data points?

2. Are there any disadvantages to calculating the mean absolute deviation or interquartile range from multiple samples for a population that consists of very few data points? Explain your reasoning.

Be prepared to share you solutions and methods.

14

Student	5. About how much time do you spend doing homework each week?
1-Sue (F)	120 minutes
2-Jorge (M)	60 minutes
3-Alex (M)	100 minutes
4-Maria (F)	100 minutes
5-Tamika(F)	150 minutes
6-Sarah (F)	10 minutes
7-Beth (F)	45 minutes
8-Sam (M)	300 minutes
9-Eric (M)	60 minutes
10-Marcus(M)	50 minutes
11-Carla (F)	150 minutes
12-Ben (M)	60 minutes
13-Will (M)	120 minutes
14-Yasmin(F)	50 minutes
15-Paulos(M)	30 minutes
16-Jon (M)	150 minutes
17-Rose (F)	200 minutes
18-Donna(F)	90 minutes
19-Suzi (F)	90 minutes
20-Kayla (F)	200 minutes

14

14.5 TAKING A SURVEY
Using Sample Size

Learning Goals

In this lesson, you will:

▶ Investigate the sample size of a survey.

▶ Investigate the concept that as the sample size increases, the statistic obtained gets closer to the actual population parameter.

Key Term

▶ sample size

Communication has evolved over time, and technology has been a contributor to this evolution—to some grammarians distaste. With the technology of text messaging, some grammarians are fearful that good grammar and language are in danger. This is due to the misspelled words, incorrect tense, and abbreviations of words in texts. On the other hand, text supporters claim that instant communication is very important to our society. Do you think grammar will deteriorate with the progress of communication? Do you think that other school subjects could also deteriorate with technological progress?

A grammarian is a person who is an expert in grammar. Make sure you use the correct tense and subject verb agreement when you talk to grammarians!

14

Problem 1 Did You Get My Text?

 Cell phone companies offer many service plans with different features. Text messaging is one feature a customer can consider when purchasing a cell phone plan. Your class survey included a question about the number of texts you send in one day.

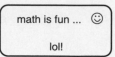
math is fun ... ☺

lol!

1. Suppose a phone company decided to estimate the number of texts pre-teens and teenagers in the United States send by using the results of your class survey.

   a. What is the population for this problem?

   b. What is the sample?

 c. Would the sample be a random sample? Why or why not?

 Your math teacher wants to know the mean number of text messages students send in one day. Rather than using the results from the entire class survey, she decides to take a random sample. When selecting a random sample, the number of members of the population selected to be part of the sample is called the **sample size**. For example, if your teacher selects four students for her sample, the sample size is 4. If she selects seven students, the sample size is 7.

2. Your teacher decides to select a sample of 2 students using the random digit table beginning on Line 13 shown.

   Line 13   12639 75291 71020 17265 41598 64074 64629 63293 53307 48766

   a. What is the sample size?

   b. Your teacher assigned each student a two-digit number beginning with 1. Which students are chosen for the sample?

   c. Calculate the mean number of texts these students send in one day using the sample for your class or the data set given in Lesson 14.1.

   d. Use the random number table at the end of Lesson 14.2. Begin on any line and choose two students for the sample from the class survey. Record the student number, student name, and the number of text messages sent daily.

      Student Number: _____   Name: _____

      Number of text messages sent daily: _____

      Student Number: _____   Name: _____

      Number of text messages sent daily: _____

14

e. Calculate the mean number of texts these students send in one day for your sample.

f. Compare your results to others in the class by recording the results on a dot plot

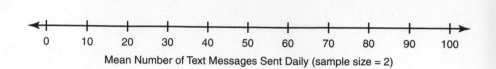

Mean Number of Text Messages Sent Daily (sample size = 2)

g. What do you notice about the dot plot?

h. What would you estimate is the mean number of texts sent?

3. Suppose your teacher decides to select a sample of 5 students from your class survey using the random number table beginning on Line 13. She starts assigning each student a two-digit number starting at 1.

a. What is the sample size?

b. Which students are chosen for the sample? If necessary, use more than one line on the random digit table. What is the mean number of text messages sent daily? (Remember that each student is assigned a two-digit number beginning with the number 1.)

c. With your partner, begin on any line of the random digit table and choose 5 students for the sample from the class survey. Record the student number, student name, and number of text messages sent in one day.

Student Number: _____   Name: _____

Number of text messages sent daily: _____

Student Number: _____   Name: _____

Number of text messages sent daily: _____

Student Number: _____   Name: _____

Number of text messages sent daily: _____

Student Number: _____   Name: _____

Number of text messages sent daily: _____

Student Number: _____   Name: _____

Number of text messages sent daily: _____

d. Calculate the mean number of texts these students send in one day.

e. Record the results of your classmates on the dot plot.

```
◄──┼────┼────┼────┼────┼────┼────┼────┼────┼────┼──►
   0   10   20   30   40   50   60   70   80   90  100
```
Mean Number of Text Messages Sent Daily (sample size = 5)

f. Compare the line plot to the dot plot when the sample size was 2. What do you notice?

g. What would you estimate the mean number of text messages sent daily to be?

14

4. What do you predict would happen to the mean number of text messages sent if yo[u] teacher took a sample of 8 students?

5. Beginning on Line 13, assign all students a two-digit number starting at 1. Select a sample of 8 students and calculate the mean number of texts students send in one day. If necessary, use more than one line on the random digit table.

   a. Which students are chosen for the sample?

   b. Compare the means from the samples of size 2, size 5, and size 8. Which mean d[o] you think is a better estimate to the actual mean number of texts students sent in one day? Explain your reasoning.

Remember that the purpose of taking a sample is to use it to learn something about the population. As the size of the sample increases, the statistic obtained from the sample gets closer to the parameter of the population. As always, the sample must be randomly chosen.

1. Describe what is displayed in the histograms shown. Is there any information missing in each histogram?

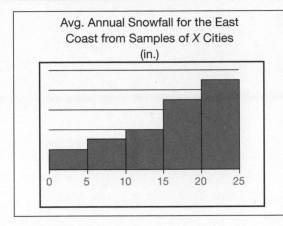

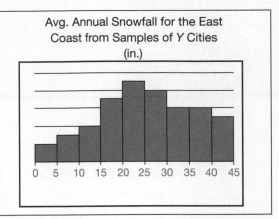

Remember the rule about the intervals of a histogram? If a data value lies on two bounds, it should be included in the bound to the right of that interval. So the data point 5 would not be included in the interval 0 and 5, but it would be included in the interval 5 and 10.

2. Joel claims the data displayed in the first histogram had a larger sample size. Paulette disagrees and says the data in the second histogram had a larger sample size. Who is correct? Explain your reasoning.

14

3. Which histogram should you use if you want to estimate the actual mean annual snowfall for the East Coast? Estimate the mean snowfall.

 Be prepared to share you solutions and methods.

Sample Class Data		
Number	**Student**	**Number of Text Messages Sent Daily**
1		
2		
3		
4		
5		
6		
7		
8		
9		
10		
11		
12		
13		
14		
15		
16		

14

14

Sample Class Data		
Number	Student	Number of Text Messages Sent Daily
17		
18		
19		
20		
21		
22		
23		
24		
25		
26		
27		
28		
29		
30		
31		
32		

Be prepared to share your solutions and methods.

14

14

Random Number Table

Line 1	65285	97198	12138	53010	94601	15838	16805	61404	43516	17020
Line 2	17264	57327	38224	29301	18164	38109	34976	65692	98566	29550
Line 3	95639	99754	31199	92558	68368	04985	51092	37780	40261	14479
Line 4	61555	76404	86214	11808	12840	55147	97438	60222	12645	62090
Line 5	78137	98768	04689	87130	79225	08153	84967	64539	79493	74917
Line 6	62490	99215	84987	28759	19107	14733	24550	28067	68894	38490
Line 7	24216	63444	21283	07044	92729	37284	13211	37485	11415	36457
Line 8	18975	95428	33226	55901	31605	43816	22259	00317	46999	98571
Line 9	59138	39542	71168	57609	91510	27904	74244	50940	31553	62562
Line 10	29478	59652	50414	31966	87912	87154	12944	49862	96566	48825
Line 11	96155	95009	27429	72918	08457	78134	48407	26061	58754	05326
Line 12	29621	66583	62966	12468	20245	14015	04014	35713	03980	03024
Line 13	12639	75291	71020	17265	41598	64074	64629	63293	53307	48766
Line 14	14544	37134	54714	02401	63228	26831	19386	15457	17999	18306
Line 15	83403	88827	09834	11333	68431	31706	26652	04711	34593	22561
Line 16	67642	05204	30697	44806	96989	68403	85621	45556	35434	09532
Line 17	64041	99011	14610	40273	09482	62864	01573	82274	81446	32477
Line 18	17048	94523	97444	59904	16936	39384	97551	09620	63932	03091
Line 19	93039	89416	52795	10631	09728	68202	20963	02477	55494	39563
Line 20	82244	34392	96607	17220	51984	10753	76272	50985	97593	34320

14

14

Key Terms

- survey (14.1)
- data (14.1)
- population (14.1)
- census (14.1)
- sample (14.1)
- parameter (14.1)
- statistic (14.1)

- random sample (14.2)
- random number generator (14.2)
- random number table (14.2)
- dot plot (line plot) (14.3)
- variability (14.4)
- spread (14.4)

- range (14.4)
- mean absolute deviation (14.4)
- deviation from the mean (14.4)
- sample size (14.5)

14.1 Differentiating Between a Census and a Sample

A census is the data collected from every member of a population. A sample is the data collected from part of a population.

Example

After surveying each of the boys in his class, Winston concludes that 50 percent of the students in his school watch cartoons on a regular basis.

The data collected are a sample because Winston did not survey each of the students in his school. He excluded the girls and the students who are not in his class.

14.1 Differentiating Between a Parameter and a Statistic

When data are gathered from a population, the characteristic used to describe the population is called a parameter. When data are gathered from a sample, the characteristic used to describe the sample is called a statistic.

Example

After conducting a survey of the students in her class, Jill concludes that 40 percent of the students in her class participate in at least one school sport. The students in Jill's class represent the population. The survey results are a parameter because it describes the population.

14

14.1 Differentiating Between Random and Non-Random Samples

A random sample is a sample that is selected from the population in such a way that every member of that population has the same chance of being selected. A non-random sample is a sample that is selected from the population, but only certain members of the population have the chance to be selected.

Example

Jerome conducts a survey of every brown-haired student in his class to determine the percentage of students in his class who enjoy skateboarding.

The sample is not random because each student did not have an equal chance of being selected.

14.2 Using a Random Number Table to Select a Random Sample

Random number tables are used to select random samples. Random number tables are tables that often contain hundreds of random digits. They usually display the numbers with a space after every five digits so that the digits are easier to read.

Example

The following random number line shows how to select two-digit numbers that start at 10 and end at 50.

Two-digit numbers are selected from left to right as shown by the arrows. Each two-digit number that falls between 10 and 50 are underlined. The five random numbers are 28, 12, 13, 30, and 10. If a two-digit number appears a second time, it should be disregarded.

14.3 Using Random Sampling

Getting statistics obtained from samples are more likely to represent the parameter of the population if the sample is randomly chosen.

Example

Mrs. Jankowski asks if anyone in her math class is interested in taking a survey about video games. She hands a survey to the first five students to raise their hands. After getting the results, Mrs. Jankowski concludes that 100 percent of the students in her class play video games daily. Believing that this statistic doesn't accurately describe the population, Mrs. Jankowski uses a random number table to randomly select five students for the survey. Based on the random sample, she concludes that 40 percent of the students in her class play video games daily. After conducting a census of the entire class, Mrs. Jankowski determines that 30 percent of the students in her math class play video games daily.

The statistic based on the original sample does not accurately describe the population because only volunteers interested in taking a survey about video games raised their hands. The random sample produced a much more accurate statistic because every student had an equal chance to participate.

14

Use Sampling and Proportional Reasoning

The selection of a random sample can help determine parameters of a population. Set up a ratio using the sample size selected to the statistic of the sample. Next, set up a proportion to estimate a parameter of the entire population based on the statistic of the sample. By performing this, the ratio is scaling up from your sample to the population.

Example

Mrs. Johnson was trying to determine the total number of siblings the students in her class have. After taking a survey of a random sample of 5 out of her 25 students, she determined that those 5 students have a total of 11 siblings. She set up a ratio and used proportional reasoning to estimate the total number of siblings for all 25 students in her class.

$$\frac{\text{number of students in the sample}}{\text{total number of siblings in the sample}} = \frac{\text{total number of students}}{\text{total number of siblings for all students}}$$

$$\frac{5}{11} = \frac{25}{x}$$

$$5x = 275$$

$$x = 55$$

Mrs. Johnson estimates that the total number of siblings for all 25 students in her class is 55.

> More girls are graduating from college in science and math than ever. You go, girls!

4.4 Analyze Measures of Center for Samples from a Population

A measure of center is the value at the center or middle of a data set. The most common measure of center is the mean, which is the value obtained by dividing the sum of a set of quantities by the number of quantities in the set. The mean of a sample from a population is not necessarily the best representation of the center of the entire population. There can be quite a difference in mean when selecting more than one sample from the same population. But the means of different samples can be used to estimate the mean of the population.

Example

A set of data includes the following values: 35, 67, 72, 60, 82, 79, 75, 78. If a sample is taken from this set that includes the first 4 numbers, the mean of the sample is $\frac{35 + 67 + 72 + 60}{4}$ = 58.5. A sample from the set that includes the last 4 numbers has a mean of $\frac{82 + 79 + 75 + 78}{4}$ = 78.5. When both means are plotted on a number line, halfway between the points is an estimate of the mean of the population. The actual mean of the whole population is $\frac{35 + 67 + 72 + 60 + 82 + 79 + 75 + 78}{8}$ = 68.5, which is the same as the estimate.

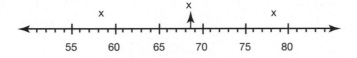

14

14.4 Analyze Measures of Variation for Samples from a Population

The distribution of data is sometimes called the variability of data. The variability of data describes how "spread out" the data is. This can also be described as the spread of data. One of the simplest measures of variability or spread is the range of data. The range of data refers to the minimum and maximum values in a data set. Another spread of data is the mean absolute deviation, or the average of the absolute values of the deviations of each data value from the mean.

Example

A sample data set includes the following values: 35, 67, 72, 60. The range of the data set is between 35 and 72. The mean of the data set is $\frac{35 + 67 + 72 + 60}{4} = 58.5$. The absolute deviation of each value is shown in the table.

Data Value	Deviation from the Mean	Absolute Deviation
35	$35 - 58.5 = -23.5$	$|-23.5| = 23.5$
67	$67 - 58.5 = 8.5$	$|8.5| = 8.5$
72	$72 - 58.5 = 13.5$	$|13.5| = 13.5$
60	$60 - 58.5 = 1.5$	$|1.5| = 1.5$

Therefore, the mean absolute deviation of the sample is $\frac{23.5 + 8.5 + 13.5 + 1.5}{4} = 11.75$

14

4.4 **Analyze Samples from a Population Using the Five Number Summary**

The five number summary is one way to analyze a data set. The five number summary consists of the:

- Minimum, which is the least data value in the entire data set,
- First Quartile (Q1), which is the median for the data values between the minimum and the median of the entire data set,
- Median, which is the number in the middle of the entire data set,
- Third Quartile (Q3), which is the median for the data values between the median of the entire data set and the maximum data value,
- Maximum, which is the greatest data value in the entire data set.

A way to graphically display a five number summary is to construct a box-and-whisker plot.

Example

A five number summary, interquartile range, and box-and-whisker plot are shown for the sample data set: 35, 67, 72, 60.

Minimum	Q1	Median	Q3	Maximum	Interquartile Range
35	$\dfrac{35 + 60}{2} = 47.5$	$\dfrac{60 + 67}{2} = 63.5$	$\dfrac{67 + 72}{2} = 69.5$	72	$69.5 - 47.5$ $= 22$

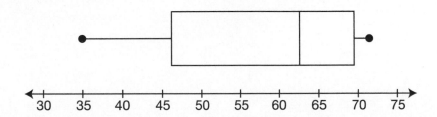

14

14.5 Understanding the Effect of Sample Size on Statistics

When selecting a sample, the number of members of the population selected to be in the sample is called the sample size. As the sample size increases, the statistic obtained gets closer to the actual population parameter.

Example

Recently, 30 students took a math test. In order to determine the class average, Cindy randomly selects a sample of five students and asks them their scores. The average score of the five students is 90. Clark randomly selects a sample of 10 students and asks them their scores. The average score of these 10 students is 85. Finally, Yuri randomly selects 15 students and asks them their scores. The average score of these 15 students is 78. The actual class average for the test is 80.

As the sample size increased, the statistic got closer to the actual parameter.

15 COMPARING POPULATIONS

Newseum is a 250,000 square foot museum that documents the history of the news and the press. They also highlight and celebrate the importance of photography and its interaction with reporting news items.

15.1

CHECKING THE PAPERS AND THE BLOGS

Comparing Measures of Center of Two Populations

Learning Goals

In this lesson, you will:

▶ Calculate the measures of center and measures of variability for two populations.

▶ Compare the difference of the measures of center for two populations to their measures of variability.

Are you a blog reader? A blog, which came from the words *web log*, is a web site on which people can write opinions or suggestions about almost any topic or subject. Blogs also allow blog readers to submit comments to opinions on a blog. According to some experts, blogs have also become another way for people to network and socialize.

As of 2010, there are an *estimated* 120,000,000 to 400,000,000 English-language blogs on the Internet. If you're wondering why the range of this estimate is so big, it is because every day brand-new blogs are started on various websites. On those same days, thousands upon thousands of blogs are considered abandoned because of lack of activity. Experts also believe that approximately 300,000,000 to 600,000,000 people regularly read English-language blogs—and that number jumps to an estimated 1 billion to 2 billion readers of non-English blogs. Another way to think of this is that approximately 1 in 3 people read blogs. So, are you a blog reader?

Problem 1   How Many Blogs Do You Read?

Mr. Camacho is planning a trip to Newseum in Washington, D.C. A major media compan
promises to pay the expenses of the trip just as long as each student reads 10 blogs in
one month. As an added bonus, the media company will offer either all the girls or all the
boys a gift certificate for $100 each to use at the Newseum gift shop once they determin
which group consistently reads blogs regularly throughout the month. The media compa
is *not* determining which group reads the most total blogs in one month. If each group
consistently reads the same amount of blogs, then they will determine which group read
the most total blogs in a month. The blog-reading results are shown in the table.

Student Girls (G) Boys (B)	About how many blogs do you read in one month?	Student Girls (G) Boys (B)	About how many blogs do you read in one month?
Sue (G)	50	Carla (G)	70
Jorge (B)	20	Ben (B)	30
Alex (B)	30	Will (B)	40
Maria (G)	100	Yasmin (G)	70
Tamika (G)	60	Paulos (B)	20
Sarah (G)	80	Jon (B)	60
Beth (G)	60	Rose (G)	80
Sam (B)	10	Donde (B)	20
Eric (B)	30	Suzi (G)	60
Marcus (B)	40	Kayla (G)	70

1. Display the results on a dot plot. Use an "o" to represent the boys' responses, and use an "x" to represent the girls' responses from the information in the table about Simon's class.

Number of Blogs Read (Per month)

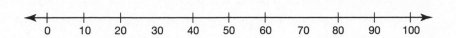

2. What observations can you make from your dot plot?

3. Describe the distribution of data values for each the boys and the girls.

4. Analyze the data values on your dot plot for the boys and for the girls.

   a. Estimate the mean number of blogs the boys read in a month. Mark the mean on your dot plot with a "B." Explain how you determined your estimate.

   b. Estimate the mean number of blogs the girls read in a month. Mark the mean on your dot plot with a "G." Explain how you determined your estimate.

5. Calculate the actual mean number of blogs the girls read in a month.

6. Calculate the actual mean number of blogs the boys read in a month.

7. What observations can you make about the spread of the two data sets?

8. Complete the table and calculate the mean absolute deviation for the number of blogs the girls and boys read per month.

Blogs Read by Boys (per month)	Deviation from the Mean	Absolute Deviation from the Mean	Blogs Read by Girls (per month)	Deviation from the Mean	Absolute Deviation from the Mean
20			50		
30			100		
10			60		
30			80		
40			60		
30			70		
40			70		
20			80		
60			60		
20			70		
Mean Absolute Deviation			**Mean Absolute Deviation**		

9. Interpret and compare the mean absolute deviations for both the girls and the boys.

10. How can you tell by looking at your dot plot that the mean absolute deviations would be equal for boys and girls?

11. Can the media company determine a winner of which group consistently reads blogs throughout the month? Explain your reasoning.

12. How does the difference between the two means compare to the mean absolute deviations?

13. Which group will be declared the winner of the $100 gift certificate to Newseum's gift shop? How did the media company determine the winner?

Problem 2 Football Scores

When a professional or collegiate team is winning, praises go to the athletes *and* coaches. However, when a team is struggling, the coach usually receives the blame. Sometimes, coaches are undeserving of this blame. Coaches and team owners will often look to data (especially from year to year) to see if a coach is underachieving, or if the coach is performing well, but the team is just not doing enough to win games.

One data set that coaches and team owners may analyze is the number of points scored during one or many seasons. Coaches may want to compare their teams' performances from one year to another year.

In 2009, the Los Alamos Middle School's football team only won 2 games. The school decided to give the coach another chance at improving the team the next year. In 2010, the team won 7 games. Did scoring points have something to do with Los Alamos improving their record? The stem-and-leaf plot shows the number of points scored in each game by Los Alamos Middle School's football team in 2009 and 2010.

Los Alamos Middle School Football Team

Points scored 2009						Points scored 2010			
		7	3	0	0				
7	4	4	2	0	1	4	7	7	
			9	8	2	4	7	8	8
				5	3	5	8		
					4	2	5		

Key = 0|3 means 3

1. Which year did the Los Alamos Middle School football team score more points?

2. Describe the distribution of the stem-and-leaf plots for each year.

How do I describe the stem-and-leaf plot for 2009? I know that I can rotate the stem-and-leaf plot counterclockwise for 2010, but what do I do for 2009? I can't rotate it and be able to visualize the distribution because the stem will go backward like the negative side of a number line!

That's true! One thing you can do is to represent the side-by-side stem-and-leaf plot as two separate stem-and-leaf plots. Then, you can rotate each stem-and-leaf plot and be able to describe the data. Can you think of other ways to be able to accurately describe the distribution of data?

3. Determine the five number summary and IQR for each data set. Then, complete the table shown.

	2009	2010
Minimum		
Q1		
Median		
Q3		
Maximum		
IQR		

4. Compare the measures of center (the median) and the IQR for the two data sets.

5. How does the difference in the medians compare to the IQR?

6. Do you think that scoring more points may have been one reason the Los Alamos Middle School football team improved its record?

Talk the Talk

1. Do you think that you can determine the mean and the spread of data for two populations from a graph or dot plot?

2. If the measures of center for two populations are equivalent, how can the mean absolute variation show the differences in variability for two populations?

Be prepared to share your solutions and methods.

15.2

CAN PODCASTS AFFECT RATINGS?

Comparing Measures of Center of Two Populations

15

Learning Goals

In this lesson, you will:

▶ Compare the measures of center for random samples from two populations.

▶ Use measures of center to draw conclusions about two populations.

Commercials and advertisements are common to see and hear in the world around us. Advertisers routinely buy airtime on radio and television to rub commercials to potential buyers. But, did you know that airtime costs different amounts at different times? For example, some of the most expensive airtime occurs during the National Football League's Super Bowl in February. Other expensive airtimes occur during popular television shows.

One way advertisers can determine the popularity of a show is to consult the Nielsen ratings, which uses statistical sampling to determine the characteristics of the television viewer population. To this day, television networks use Nielsen ratings to set the price of commercial airtime.

However, in the last few years, podcasts and digital video recorders (DVRs) have been affecting ratings. With podcasts, viewers (and in radio, listeners) do not need to commit to a certain time during the week to watch a television show. Thus, some advertisers feel that Nielsen ratings might not be accurate. And, most DVRs have a way of fast-forwarding past commercials—so advertisers are reluctant to pay premium prices for airtime. What ways do you think ratings could be recorded more accurately in a podcast and DVR world? Do you think that podcasts and DVRs can continue to affect airtime price in the future?

Problem 1 Downloading Podcasts

Square Roots is a radio show that airs 10 times a week on local radio station WMTH.

WMTH is trying to raise its commercial airtime rates during *Square Roots*. The station claims that this music show is not only heard by hundreds of middle school students, bu that there are actually more middle school students who download the podcasts regular Advertisers disagree with WMTH's claim. Advertisers want the station to verify its claim that there are more students listening by downloaded podcasts than actual listeners. To do so, WMTH and the advertisers choose Bryce Middle School to collect data. They sen out a survey and ask the following two questions:

- Do you listen to *Square Roots* on the radio or download the podcast?
- How often to you listen to *Square Roots* per week?

Fortunately, all 389 students Bryce Middle School responded to the survey.

1. What are the two populations for the *Square Roots* survey WMTH is conducting?

WMTH then decides to select a random sample for each population.

2. There are 180 regular radio listeners and 209 podcast listeners at Bryce Middle School. Describe how WMTH and the advertisers can randomly select students for their sample?

3. Use the random number table and the list of radio listeners and podcast listeners in Bryce Middle School at the end of chapter to help WMTH randomly select a sample.

a. Begin on Line 1 and randomly select 10 radio listeners. Record each student's last name in the table. Then, use the list to record the number times each student listened to *Square Roots* during the week.

Student's Last Name	Radio Shows Listened (per week)

Remember, you can also use a graphing calculator to select samples. You can use the random number generator if a random number table is not available.

b. Begin on Line 10 and randomly select 10 podcast listeners. Record each studer
last name in the table. Then, use the list to record the number of podcasts each
student downloaded in one week.

Student's Last Name	Podcasts Downloaded (per week)

> Remember, when you are assigning each student a number, each number should be the maximum number of digits in t' largest number of a population. Therefore, if there are 300 peopl in a population, each number assigned should be three digits.

4. Construct dot plots for each group using the same intervals. What conclusions can you make?

Radio Shows Listened
(per week)

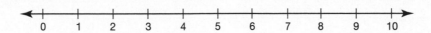

Number of Podcasts Downloaded
(per week)

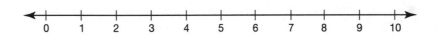

5. Describe the distribution for each graph. Describe any clusters or gaps of the data values in each graph.

6. Estimate the mean number of podcasts downloaded for each dot plot. Explain how you determined your estimate.

7. Calculate the mean number of radio shows listened in a week, and the mean number of podcasts downloaded in a week.

8. When comparing the two samples, are more shows listened to on the radio, or more podcasts downloaded?

9. Richard says, "If we had started on a different line number in the random number table, our results would have been the same." Is Richard correct? Explain your reasoning.

10. Repeat the sampling procedure by beginning on a different line number for each population. Record your results in the tables.

Radio Listeners		Podcast Listeners	
Student's Last Name	Radio Shows Listened (per week)	Student's Last Name	Podcasts Downloaded (per week)

11. Construct dot plots for each group using the same scale.

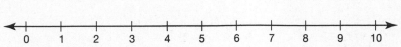

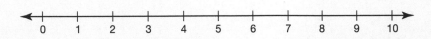

12. Describe the distribution for the shows listened to on the radio dot plot. Describe any clusters or gaps of the data values. What conclusions can you make from this dot plot?

13. Describe the distribution for the podcasts downloaded dot plot. Describe any clusters or gaps of the data values. What conclusions can you make from this dot plot?

14. Estimate the mean data values for each dot plot. Explain how you determined your estimate.

15. Calculate the mean data values for each sample.

16. When comparing the two samples, which way do fans of *Square Roots* tune in to listen to the show?

17. Compare your results with those of your classmates. Do you think that WMTH's statement that more students download the podcast for *Square Roots* than listen on the radio is true? Explain your reasoning.

Problem 2   Just You Wait!

Ratings are not limited to television shows alone. Ratings can also be used to show people's opinions of hotels and restaurants. One of the things that can help a restaurant get good ratings is the time it takes to be seated (the wait time) at a restaurant without reservations.

Big Al's Steak House and Trail's End both claim to have the shortest wait times in town. To check out the claims, Ramon, a restaurant reviewer, records the time it takes to be seated without reservations. The results of wait times for 8 visits to each restaurant are shown in the table.

Big Al's Steak House Wait Times (minutes)	Trail's End Wait Times (minutes)
5	11
13	19
22	14
7	14
20	15
21	20
20	10
12	17

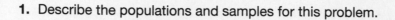

1. Describe the populations and samples for this problem.

2. Calculate the mean wait times between the two restaurants. Which restaurant seems to have faster service?

3. Complete the side-by-side stem-and-leaf plot of the times. What do you notice?

Big Al's Steak House		Trail's End

4. Determine the median wait time for each restaurant.

5. Explain the difference in median times for the two restaurants.

6. Which measure of center would you use if:

    a. you are Big Al's Steak House and want to claim you have the shortest wait time?

    b. you are Trail's End and want to claim you have the shortest wait time?

    c. you are a customer and want the shortest wait time?

7. Suppose another restaurant reviewer records wait times at each restaurant several times. Do you think it is possible that the wait times might be different from Ramon's wait times? Explain your reasoning.

8. How could we be more certain which restaurant has the shortest wait time?

Talk the Talk

1. Describe how to compare two populations. What are ways to compare each population?

2. Do you think it is important to accompany a measure of center with a graphical display when comparing the data of two populations?

3. How do you determine which measure of center to use when comparing the data of two populations?

Be prepared to share your solutions and methods.

FINDING YOUR SPOT TO LIVE

15.3

Drawing Conclusions About Two Populations

Learning Goals

In this lesson, you will:

▶ Compare the measures of variability for random samples from two populations.

▶ Use measures of variability to draw conclusions about two populations.

With the world becoming more connected through technology and travel, more and more people are leaving their hometowns to move to other parts of the country. For high school graduates who are attending college, this may be the time to move to another city or state. For job seekers, getting a job might be easier in another state. For people retiring from their jobs, moving to a warmer climate might be the ticket to comfort and relaxation—and more pleasant winters! Whatever the reason, people are on the move in the United States. So, have you ever thought about living in another part of the country? A different city? What factors would you think about if you moved to another place?

Problem 1   Comparing Temperatures

Dominique graduated from college and now has a choice of two jobs. One of the jobs is Ashland, and the other job is in Belsano. Since Dominique enjoys mild weather and average temperatures in the 60s (°F), she decides to compare the monthly average temperatures of the two cities. She gathered the following sample of average monthly temperatures for a previous year for the two cities as shown in the table.

Month	Ashland Average Monthly Temperatures (°F)	Belsano Average Monthly Temperatures (°F)
January	56	48
February	58	55
March	60	59
April	61	62
May	65	66
June	70	69
July	75	78
August	82	88
September	73	82
October	68	69
November	60	59
December	56	49

1. What are some ways Dominique could analyze the data to determine which city is warmer?

2. Dominique decides to calculate the mean and median temperature for each city to determine which city is warmer overall. Calculate the mean temperature for both cities. What do you notice?

3. Jacqui says that since Ashland and Belsano have very similar mean and median temperatures, Dominique could choose either city to live in because they both have mild temperatures. Do you agree or disagree? Explain your reasoning.

4. Construct a back-to-back stem-and-leaf plot for the average monthly temperature for each city.

Ashland | Belsano

Do not forget to add a key to the plot.

5. What conclusions can you draw from the plot?

6. Determine and interpret the five number summary and IQR for each data set. Then, describe some observations from the data of each five number summary.

	Ashland	Belsano
Minimum:		
Q1:		
Median:		
Q3:		
Maximum:		
IQR:		

7. Construct and label box-and-whisker plots for each data set using the same number line for both. What conclusions can you make?

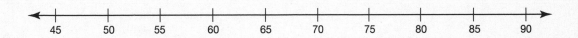

8. If you were Dominique, which city would you choose to live in? Explain your reasoning.

Problem 2   Phone Calls

Phone companies often analyze customer phone usage to see if there are patterns or trends. Gaining information about patterns helps phone companies offer different types of phone plans.

A sample of cell phone customers from the Horizon and Dash companies are shown in the histograms. The histograms display the number of calls made, and the number of minutes per phone call.

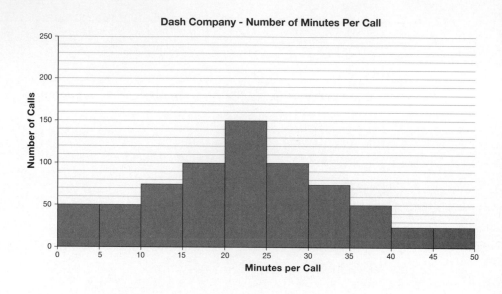

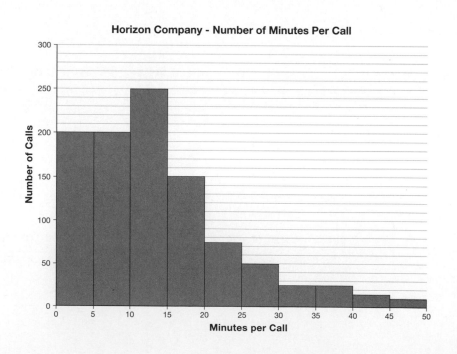

1. Describe the populations for this problem.

2. Describe the samples for this problem.

3. What do the intervals along the x-axis represent for each company?

4. What do the numbers along the y-axis represent for each company?

5. About how many phone calls were in the sample for Horizon? For Dash? Explain how you determined your answer.

6. Desmond claims that the variability in the length of phone calls for each company in terms of the range is about the same for both companies. Do you agree or disagree?

7. Describe the shape of each histogram and explain what this means in terms of the number of minutes per call.

8. Determine whether the mean or the median is the greater measure of center for each company. Then, explain why that measure of center is greater for each company.

9. If you calculate the mean absolute deviation for the length of phone calls, which company would have more variation in the length of phone calls? Why?

10. The box-and-whisker plots shown represent the cell phone call durations for Horizon and Dash. Using the information you know from the histograms for each company, which box plot do you think represents the call durations for Horizon, and which represents the call durations for Dash? Explain your choice.

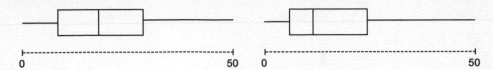

11. In terms of the box-and-whisker plots, which company has more variation in the length of phone calls? Explain your reasoning.

12. Which company might have more difficulty coming up with different cell phone plans? Why?

15

1. What can you use to determine the measures of spread for two populations?

2. Can you make conclusions about the characteristics of a population from analyzing the measure of spread for random samples of each population? Why or why not.

Be prepared to share your solutions and methods.

5.1 Comparing Measures of Center and Measures of Variability from Two Populations

The means and variations for two populations can be determined and compared visually from a graph or plot. When the measures of variation for two populations are equal or close to being equal, the difference in the means can be expressed in terms of the variation.

Example

The math test scores from Class 1 and Class 2 are shown in a side-by-side stem-and-leaf plot.

Test Scores

Class 1					Class 2			
		6	5					
	9	8	6	3				
8	4	2	7	4	6	6		
6	5	0	8	5	7	8	9	
		1	9	5	6			

	Class 1	Class 2
Minimum	56	63
Q1	69	76
Median	76	86
Q3	85	89
Maximum	91	96
IQR	85 − 69 = 16	89 − 76 = 13

15.1 The stem-and-leaf plot for Class 1's data is fairly symmetric and Class 2's data is skewed slightly left. It would be expected that the mean and median for Class 1 to be equal and the mean to be slightly less than the median for Class 2. The mean for Class 1 is 75.9 and the median is 76, so the visual representation of the data is accurate. The mean for Class 2 is 82.9 and the median is 86, so the visual representation of the data is accurate.

Comparing the centers of measure for each population indicates that Class 2 performed better on the test than Class 1. It can also be determined that a single low score brought the average down even though the median indicates that the class in general scored higher than the mean suggests.

Looking at the five number summary, the IQR shows a wider range of scores in Class 1 than in Class 2. The mean absolute deviation for Class 1 is 8.1 and for Class 2 it is 8.52. This indicates that students in Class 1 scored slightly closer to the class average than the students in Class 2.

15.2 Comparing the Measures of Center from Random Samples to Draw Conclusions about Two Populations

Taking samples from each population and calculating and comparing the measures of center is a way to compare the characteristics of two populations. It is important to accompany measures of center with a graphical display to determine if there are differences in the graphs of the samples from two populations. Analyzing data can help determine what the distribution of the data values are. Determining the distribution can help determine which measure of center to use to compare the two populations.

Example

The 100 6th graders at Miller Middle School were divided into two groups. Group 1 tutored 3rd grade students in math and Group 2 did not tutor. A random number table was used to choose 5 students as a sample from each group. The 50 students from Group 1 were each assigned a two-digit number from 21 to 70, so the first 5 two-digit numbers between 21 and 70 are chosen from Line 1. The 50 students from Group 2 were each assigned a two-digit number from 41 to 90, so the first 5 two-digit numbers between 41 and 90 are chosen from Line 2.

Line 1: 65285   97198   12138   53010   94601   15838   16805   61004   43516   1702(

Line 2: 17264   57327   38224   29301   31381   38109   34976   65692   98566   2955(

The five students with student numbers of 65, 28, 59, 30, and 60 were chosen from Group 1. The five students with student numbers of 45, 73, 42, 81, and 66 were chosen from Group 2.

The 6th grade end-of-grade math evaluation is scored on a scale of 0–6. The students' scores from the sample groups are shown on two dot plots.

Group 1

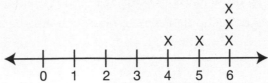

Group 2

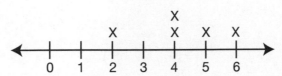

The graph for Group 1 is skewed left and the graph for Group 2 seems to be symmetric. There are no gaps in Group 1, but a cluster at 6. There is a gap at 3 in Group 2 and no real clusters. An estimate of the mean of Group 1 is between 5 and 6 and an estimate of the mean of Group 2 is between 4 and 5. The actual mean for Group 1 is $\frac{27}{5}$, or 5.4 and for Group 2 is $\frac{21}{5}$, or 4.2.

Because the graph for Group 1 is skewed left, it would be expected that the median would be greater than the mean. Because the graph for Group 2 is symmetric, the mean and median should be near equal. The teacher sponsor of the tutoring program would want to use the median as a measure of center to encourage the school to continue his program because the median of Group 1 is 6 which is greater than the mean, and the median of Group 2 is 4, which is slightly less than the mean. The teacher could use the medians to draw the conclusion that the tutoring program helps students increase their math skills overall.

15.3 Comparing the Measures of Variability from Random Samples to Draw Conclusions about Two Populations

In a case where the mean and median for two populations are close to equal, a five number summary and box-and-whisker plot are useful in determining measures of variability for two populations. Conclusions can be made about the characteristics of a population by measuring the spread of random samples of each population. Because the sample is random, the data should give accurate characteristics of each population.

Example

Data were collected from two rival airlines indicating how long after the stated departure times the flights actually left the gate. Random samples were chosen from each set of data.

Departure Time Differences

My Air				Fly High		
5	0	0	7	8	9	
9 5	1	1	7	8	9	9
6 0	0	2	4	7	9	
4 3	3	3	0			
	0	4	9			

	My Air	Fly High
Minimum	0	7
Q1	13	13
Median	20	19
Q3	33	28
Maximum	40	49
IQR	33 − 13 = 20	28 − 13 = 15

812 • **Chapter 15** Comparing Populations

My Air

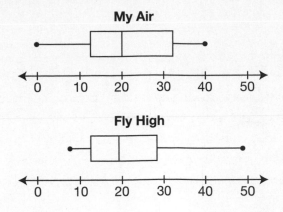

Fly High

The mean for both airlines is 21.3. The medians for both airlines are also close at 20 and 19. So, to notice a difference between the two airlines, the variability must be considered. The plot for My Air is fairly symmetric and the plot for Fly High is skewed right. The box-and-whisker plots indicate that 50% of My Air's times are more spread out than 50% of Fly High's times. While Fly High has a larger range overall, the IQR is smaller than My Air's. So, a passenger looking for an airline with consistently less departure delays, they should choose Fly High over My Air.

Thanks for all your help with this chapter! Nice work!

Square Root Fans Who Listen on the Radio

Student Number	Student Name	Radio Shows Listened (per week)	Student Number	Student Name	Radio Shows Listened (per week)
1	Abunto	1	20	Cuthbert	6
2	Adler	3	21	D'Ambrosio	0
3	Aizawa	3	22	Datz	4
4	Alescio	4	23	Delecroix	2
5	Almasy	8	24	Difiore	6
6	Ansari	6	25	Dobrich	7
7	Aro	7	26	Donoghy	1
8	Aung	2	27	Donaldson	5
9	Baehr	7	28	Dreher	2
10	Bellmer	1	29	Dubinsky	1
11	Bilski	4	30	Dytko	8
12	Blinn	6	31	Fabry	7
13	Bonetto	3	32	Fetcher	1
14	Breznai	1	33	Fontes	5
15	Cabot	3	34	Frick	3
16	Chacalos	0	35	Furmanek	5
17	Cioc	0	36	Gadgil	4
18	Cole	3	37	Gavlak	4
19	Creighan	4	38	Gibbs	0

Student Number	Student Name	Radio Shows Listened (per week)
39	Gloninger	2
40	Goff	1
41	Granger	0
42	Guca	2
43	Haag	8
44	Heese	5
45	Hilson	1
46	Holihan	1
47	Hudack	1
48	Ianuzzi	3
49	Islamov	4
50	Jacobsen	5
51	Jessell	4
52	Ji	1
53	Johnson	2
54	Jomisko	1
55	Jones	6
56	Joy	5
57	Jumba	1

Student Number	Student Name	Radio Shows Listened (per week)
58	Juth	7
59	Jyoti	6
60	Kachur	2
61	Kanai	0
62	Keller	2
63	Khaing	7
64	Kindler	5
65	Kneiss	5
66	Kolc	1
67	Kuisis	2
68	Labas	1
69	Lasek	8
70	Leeds	5
71	Lin	0
72	Litsko	2
73	Lodi	3
74	Lookman	2
75	Lucini	1
76	Lykos	0

Student Number	Student Name	Radio Shows Listened (per week)
77	MacAllister	1
78	Magliocca	6
79	Marchick	5
80	McGuire	1
81	McNary	7
82	Meadows	0
83	Merks	8
84	Mickler	5
85	Minniti	4
86	Mohr	3
87	Mordecki	5
88	Mueser	3
89	Musati	3
90	Myron	2
91	Nadzam	4
92	Nazif	7
93	Newby	0
94	Ng	1
95	Nino	2

Student Number	Student Name	Radio Shows Listened (per week)
96	Northcutt	4
97	Novi	3
98	Null	8
99	New	5
100	Nyiri	1
101	Nzuyen	2
102	O'Bryon	0
103	Obitz	3
104	Oglesby	8
105	Ono	1
106	Paclawski	0
107	Pappis	6
108	Peery	3
109	Phillips	5
110	Potter	3
111	Pribanic	7
112	Pwono	5
113	Quinn	2
114	Rabel	5

15

Student Number	Student Name	Radio Shows Listened (per week)
115	Rayl	2
116	Rea	4
117	Reynolds	5
118	Rhor	8
119	Rielly	8
120	Risa	7
121	Robinson	8
122	Roethlein	1
123	Romanski	7
124	Rouce	7
125	Rubio	7
126	Rutland	3
127	Rychcik	1
128	Sabhnani	6
129	Sandroni	2
130	Saxon	3
131	Scalo	4
132	Schessler	1
133	Seeley	0
134	Shanahan	3

Student Number	Student Name	Radio Shows Listened (per week)
135	Siejk	1
136	Skaro	3
137	Slonaker	8
138	Sobr	2
139	Spatz	4
140	Sramac	2
141	Stevens	4
142	Tabor	0
143	Tevis	5
144	Thomas	0
145	Thompson	1
146	Thorne	1
147	Tiani	0
148	Tokay	6
149	Toomey	6
150	Trax	1
151	Truong	8
152	Tunstall	1
153	Twiss	6
154	Tyler	0

Student Number	Student Name	Radio Shows Listened (per week)	Student Number	Student Name	Radio Shows Listened (per week)
155	Ueki	0	168	Wilson	4
156	Uriah	6	169	Woller	1
157	Vagnelli	6	170	Woo	0
158	Van Dine	5	171	Wunderlich	6
159	Vella	1	172	Wycoff	4
160	Vidnic	0	173	Xander	8
161	Volk	5	174	Yahya	0
162	Vyra	4	175	Yezovich	4
163	Wadhwani	5	176	Youse	0
164	Warnaby	0	177	Yuzon	8
165	Weasley	2	178	Za Khai	3
166	Weidt	8	179	Ziff	2
167	Whitelow	0	180	Zuk	5

15

Square Roots Fans Who Download Show Podcasts

Student Number	Student Name	Podcasts Downloaded (per week)	Student Number	Student Name	Podcasts Downloaded (per week)
1	Aaronson	2	21	Chang	4
2	Abati	0	22	Clarke	9
3	Ackerman	4	23	Crnkovich	0
4	Aderholt	2	24	Dahl	0
5	Akat	7	25	Dax	7
6	Aleck	9	26	Defoe	1
7	Alessandro	5	27	Dengler	4
8	Allen	3	28	Di Minno	4
9	Ansil	1	29	Dilla	5
10	Archer	5	30	Draus	5
11	Badgett	9	31	Duffy	0
12	Bartle	2	32	Ecoff	3
13	Bibby	9	33	Esparra	7
14	Bilich	5	34	Fakiro	7
15	Bloom	3	35	Ferlan	4
16	Boccio	5	36	Fetherman	2
17	Bracht	3	37	Fillipelli	6
18	Bujak	7	38	Fisher	2
19	Caliari	9	39	Folino	9
20	Cerminara	8	40	Forrester	9

Student Number	Student Name	Podcasts Downloaded (per week)
41	Frena	1
42	Galdi	8
43	Gansberger	3
44	Gianni	1
45	Glencer	1
46	Godec	7
47	Goldstein	0
48	Graef	6
49	Gula	1
50	Hagen	2
51	Haupt	8
52	Herc	4
53	Hnat	9
54	Hodak	3
55	Hoyt	2
56	Huang	3
57	Iannotta	4
58	Irwin	5
59	Jackson	7
60	Jamil	1

Student Number	Student Name	Podcasts Downloaded (per week)
61	Jessop	1
62	Johnson	9
63	Joos	9
64	Joseph	5
65	Jubic	3
66	Juhl	7
67	Jung	9
68	Jurgensen	4
69	Jyoti	0
70	Kaib	5
71	Kapoor	6
72	Kennedy	2
73	Kimel	5
74	Klaas	4
75	Ko	9
76	Krabb	1
77	Ladley	9
78	Lawson	1
79	Lemieux	7
80	Lewan	6

15

Student Number	Student Name	Podcasts Downloaded (per week)
81	Ling	6
82	Loch	4
83	Lorenzo	4
84	Lovejoy	5
85	Luba	8
86	Lukitsch	4
87	Luzzi	8
88	Lyman	5
89	MacIntyre	8
90	Maddex	5
91	Marai	2
92	Mato	9
93	McCaffrey	0
94	McElroy	5
95	McMillan	3
96	Meng	9
97	Michelini	5
98	Misra	0
99	Miller	8
100	Modecki	7

Student Number	Student Name	Podcasts Downloaded (per week)
101	Moorey	6
102	Mox	7
103	Mrkali	7
104	Mu	0
105	Muller	3
106	Murphy	2
107	Mwambazi	6
108	Myers	4
109	Nangle	3
110	Neilan	7
111	Nicolay	5
112	Niehl	6
113	Nix	2
114	Noga	3
115	Nowatzki	7
116	Nuescheler	5
117	Nye	6
118	Nytra	6
119	O'Carrol	6
120	Obedi	7

Student Number	Student Name	Podcasts Downloaded (per week)	Student Number	Student Name	Podcasts Downloaded (per week)
121	Oehrle	8	142	Renard	7
122	Olds	5	143	Rex	7
123	Oleary	0	144	Richards	7
124	Ondrey	1	145	Ridout	7
125	Owusu	9	146	Rivera	6
126	Palamides	9	147	Roberts	4
127	Pappas	0	148	Rodwich	0
128	Pecori	3	149	Roney	7
129	Pennix	4	150	Ross	6
130	Pendleton	1	151	Rothering	0
131	Phillippi	2	152	Rua	4
132	Pieton	6	153	Russo	8
133	Ploeger	2	154	Ryer	8
134	Pressman	4	155	Sagi	8
135	Puzzini	1	156	Sallinger	6
136	Qu	4	157	Sau	7
137	Qutyan	8	158	Sbragia	7
138	Raab	5	159	Schaier	5
139	Raeff	0	160	Schmit	2
140	Rav	1	161	Scopaz	4
141	Rea	5	162	Sebula	4

15

Student Number	Student Name	Podcasts Downloaded (per week)
163	Shah	1
164	Sidor	6
165	Skraly	6
166	Sokolowski	5
167	Speer	6
168	T'Ung	9
169	Tamar	9
170	Tebelius	1
171	Tesla	4
172	Thuma	0
173	Tibi	2
174	Tobkes	9
175	Torelli	8
176	Tozzi	0
177	Traut	6
178	Trax	0
179	Tu	8
180	Tumicki	2
181	Tyson	1
182	Uansa	0
183	Ulan	4

Student Number	Student Name	Podcasts Downloaded (per week)
184	Urbano	7
185	Uzonyi	7
186	Vaezi	8
187	Vinay	6
188	Vu	8
189	Wallee	0
190	Waldock	4
191	Wallace	2
192	Webb	9
193	Weisenfeld	0
194	Whalen	7
195	Wiley	9
196	Williams	5
197	Williamson	6
198	Witek	9
199	Wojcik	3
200	Woollett	6
201	Wulandana	8
202	Wysor	9
203	Xiao	4
204	Yee	6

Student Number	Student Name	Podcasts Downloaded (per week)
205	Yost	1
206	Young	7
207	Yuros	6

Student Number	Student Name	Podcasts Downloaded (per week)
208	Zaki	0
209	Zimmerman	1

15

Random Number Table

Line 1	65285	97198	12138	53010	94601	15838	16805	61004	43516	1702(
Line 2	17264	57327	38224	29301	31381	38109	34976	65692	98566	2955(
Line 3	95639	99754	31199	92558	68368	04985	51092	37780	40261	14479
Line 4	61555	76404	86210	11808	12841	45147	97438	60022	12645	6200(
Line 5	78137	98768	04689	87130	79225	08153	84967	64539	79493	74917
Line 6	62490	99215	84987	28759	19177	14733	24550	28067	68894	3849(
Line 7	24216	63444	21283	07044	92729	37284	13211	37485	10415	3645i
Line 8	16975	95428	33226	55903	31605	43817	22250	03918	46999	9850i
Line 9	59138	39542	71168	57609	91510	77904	74244	50940	31553	62562
Line 10	29478	59652	50414	31966	87912	87154	12944	49862	96566	48825
Line 11	96155	95009	27429	72918	08457	78134	48407	26061	58754	05326
Line 12	29621	66583	62966	12468	20245	14015	04014	35713	03980	03024
Line 13	12639	75291	71020	17265	41598	64074	64629	63293	53307	48766
Line 14	14544	37134	54714	02401	63228	26831	19386	15457	17999	18306
Line 15	83403	88827	09834	11333	68431	31706	26652	04711	34593	22561
Line 16	67642	05204	30697	44806	96989	68403	85621	45556	35434	09532
Line 17	64041	99011	14610	40273	09482	62864	01573	82274	81446	32477
Line 18	17048	94523	97444	59904	16936	39384	97551	09620	63932	03091
Line 19	93039	89416	52795	10631	09728	68202	20963	02477	55494	39563
Line 20	82244	34392	96607	17220	51984	10753	76272	50985	97593	34320

16 INTRODUCTION TO PROBABILITY

During the spring and summer days in the United States, weather forecasters verishly review computer models and atmospheric pressure. These tors and others help forecasters redict the chances of a tornado forming. Many times, these predictions can save many lives during bad weather.

16

16.1

ROLLING, ROLLING, ROLLING . . .

Defining and Representing Probability

16

Learning Goals

In this lesson, you will:

▶ Differentiate between an outcome and an event for an experiment.

▶ List the sample space for an experiment.

▶ Determine the probability for an event.

▶ Understand that the probability for an event is between 0 and 1 that can be expressed as a fraction, decimal, or percent.

▶ Determine that the sum of the probabilities of the outcomes of an experiment is always 1.

Key Terms

▶ outcome

▶ experiment

▶ sample space

▶ event

▶ simple event

▶ probability

▶ equally likely

The weatherman forecasts a 60% chance of rain. A new drug is reported to have a 0.5% chance of causing headaches. You have a 1 out of 4 chance of guessing the answer to a multiple-choice question with four possible answers. All of these statements have one thing in common—they attempt to predict the future. In mathematics, you can use probability to determine what *may* happen in the future. How else do you encounter probability in the real world?

Problem 1 What Are the Chances?

A six-sided number cube has one number, from 1 through 6, on each of its faces. Numbe cubes are often used when playing many board games.

1. Create a list of all the possible numbers that can appear on the top face if you roll a six-sided number cube.

The numbers 1, 2, 3, 4, 5, and 6 are the *outcomes* that can occur when rolling a six-sided number cube. An **outcome** is the result of a single trial of an *experiment*. An **experiment** is a situation involving chance that leads to results, or outcomes. A list of all possible outcomes of an experiment is called a **sample space**. A sample space is typically enclosed in brackets, { }, with commas between the outcomes.

2. List the sample space for the experiment of rolling a six-sided number cube.

An **event** is one or a group of possible outcomes for a given situation. A **simple event** is an event consisting of one outcome. For example, in the number cube experiment, an event could be rolling an even number. However, rolling a 5 is a simple event.

Probability is a measure of the likelihood that an event will occur. It is a way of assigning numerical value to the chance that an event will occur. The probability of an event is often written as *P*(event). For example, in the number cube experiment, the probability of rolling a 5 could be written as *P*(rolling a 5), or *P*(5). The probability of rolling an even number could be written as *P*(rolling an even number), or *P*(even).

In general, the way to determine the probability of an event is:

$$\text{probability} = \frac{\text{number of times an event can occur}}{\text{number of possible outcomes}}.$$

To determine the probability of rolling an odd number, or $P(odd)$, follow these steps:

Step 1: First, list all the possible outcomes.

The possible odd numbers that can be rolled are 1, 3, and 5.

Step 2: Add the number of outcomes.

There are 3 possible outcomes of rolling an odd number.

Step 3: Use the equation to determine the probability of rolling an odd number.

$$P(odd) = \frac{\text{number of times an even can occur}}{\text{number of possible outcomes}} = \frac{3 \text{ times of rolling an odd number}}{6 \text{ number of possible outcomes}}$$

The probability of rolling an odd number is 3 out of 6 outcomes.

3. What is the probability of rolling a 4, or $P(4)$? Explain your reasoning.

So, to determine $P(4)$ consider how many times a 4 can occur when you roll a six-sided number cube.

4. What is the probability of rolling a 6, or $P(6)$? Explain your reasoning.

5. Determine the probability of rolling an even number.

   a. Which outcome or outcomes make up the event of rolling an even number?

   b. Calculate the probability of rolling an even number.

6. Determine the probability of rolling a number greater than 4.

   a. Which outcome(s) make up the event of rolling a number greater than 4?

   b. Calculate the probability of rolling a number greater than 4.

Problem 2   Take A Spin!

Consider the spinner shown. Assume all sections are the same size. An experiment consists of spinning the spinner one time.

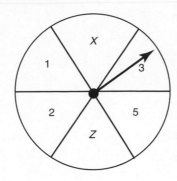

1. How many possible outcomes are there in the experiment? How did you determine your answer?

2. List the sample space for the experiment.

3. Determine the probability that the spinner lands on a letter.
   a. Describe the event.

   b. Describe the possible outcomes in this event.

   c. Calculate P(letter).

4. Determine the probability that the spinner lands on an odd number.
   a. Describe the event.

   b. Describe the possible outcomes in the event.

   c. Calculate P(odd number).

16

5. Determine the probability that the spinner lands on a vowel.

   a. Describe the event.

   b. Describe the possible outcomes in the event.

   c. Calculate P(vowel).

The Spinning Square Game is a game at the Kid Zone. The game consists of spinning th square spinner. If a player takes a spin and the spinner lands on B, the player wins a priz If the spinner lands on A, the player does not receive a prize.

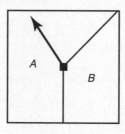

6. Predict each probability.

   a. $P(A) =$

   b. $P(B) =$

7. Britney predicts the probability that the spinner will land on A to be "7." Do you agree or disagree with Britney? Explain your reasoning.

1. What is the greatest possible probability in any experiment? Explain your reasoning.

2. What is the least possible probability in any experiment? Explain your reasoning.

3. What is the probability of an event that is just as likely to occur as not occur? Explain your reasoning.

The probability of an event occurring is a number between 0 and 1. If the event is certain to happen, then the probability is 1. If an event is impossible to happen, then the probability is 0. If an event is just as likely to happen as not happen, then the probability is 0.5, or $\frac{1}{2}$. Probabilities can be expressed as fractions, decimals, or percents.

Complete the chart representing the different probabilities.

4.

	Fraction	Decimal	Percent
P(certain event)			
P(event that is just as likely as unlikely to occur)			
P(impossible event)			

The number line shown represents the probabilities, from 0 to 1, of any event occurrin

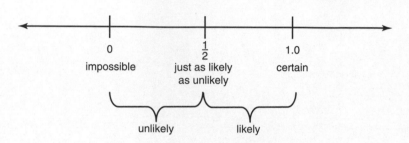

5. Estimate the probability of each event occurring. Then, place the letter correspondin to the estimated probability of the event on the number line.

	Fraction	Decimal	Percent

a. The next baby born at your local hospital will be a boy. _____ _____ _____

b. It will snow in Arizona in July. _____ _____ _____

c. You will have homework tonight. _____ _____ _____

d. You will live to be over 100 years old. _____ _____ _____

roblem 4   It's In the Bag!

Suppose there are 2 blue, 3 green, and 5 yellow marbles in a bag. One marble will be drawn from the bag.

1. List the sample space for the experiment.

2. Calculate each probability.

    a. $P(B) =$

    b. $P(G) =$

    c. $P(Y) =$

When the probabilities of all the outcomes of an experiment are equal, then the probabilities are called **equally likely**.

3. Are the probabilities in the marble experiment equally likely? Explain your reasoning.

4. Determine the sum of all the probabilities.

    $P(B) + P(G) + P(Y) =$

5. Determine the sum of the probabilities for all the outcomes of the first spinner in Problem 2.

    $P(1) + P(2) + P(3) + P(5) + P(X) + P(Z) =$

6. Do you think the sum of the probabilities for all outcomes of any experiment will always be 1? Explain your reasoning.

Talk the Talk

1. Do you think that the sum of the probabilities for all outcomes of some experiments can be greater than 1? Explain your reasoning.

2. Write an event that has a probability of 1.

3. Write an event that has a probability of 0.

 Be prepared to share your solutions and methods.

16.2

TOSS THE CUP
Determining Experimental Probability

Learning Goals

In this lesson, you will:

▶ Conduct trials of an experiment.

▶ Predict the experimental probability of an event using the results from the trials of an experiment.

▶ Use proportional reasoning to predict the probability of random events.

Key Term

▶ experimental probability

16

You are due for a win! Your luck will run out soon!

Have you ever heard someone say something like this about a game of chance? People—especially people who don't know a lot about probability—are sometimes fooled into thinking that after a long series of losses or a long series of wins that the next turn will produce different results.

Why is this thinking incorrect?

Problem 1   It's Time for the Cup Toss

Julio and Shaniqua are designing a game called Toss the Cup.

The game is played between two players. To play the game, a paper or plastic cup is needed. To start the game, the paper cup is tossed in the air.

- If the cup lands on its bottom, Player 1 wins a point.

- If the cup lands on its top, Player 2 wins wins a point.

- If the cup lands on its side, neither player receives a point.

1. List the sample space for the game.

What is your prediction?

2. Do you think all the outcomes are equally likely? Explain your reasoning.

3. Play the game 25 times with a partner. Decide who will be Player 1 and who will be Player 2.

   a. Record your results in the table using tally marks. Then, write your and your opponent's total score, and write the number of times the cup landed on its side.

Result	Tally Marks	Total
Player 1-Bottom		
Player 2-Top		
Side		

   b. Summarize your results.

Experimental probability is the ratio of the number of times an event occurs to the total number of trials performed.

$$\text{Experimental Probability} = \frac{\text{number of times the event occurs}}{\text{total number of trials performed}}$$

4. What is the experimental probability of the cup landing:

   a. on its bottom?

   b. on its top?

   c. on its side?

5. Do you think this is a fair game to play? Why or why not?

6. When you toss a six-sided number cube, the probability of it landing on any of the numbers from 1 through 6 is $\frac{1}{6}$. Is it possible to determine the exact probability of the cup landing on its top, bottom, or side? Explain your reasoning.

Examine the spinner shown.

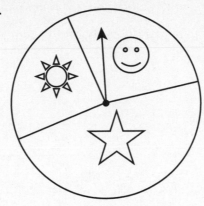

16

1. Which symbol(s) has/have the best chance for the spinner to land? Which symbol(s) has/have the worst chance for the spinner to land?

2. Predict each probability of the spinner landing on each symbol.

   a. $P(\ ☺\ ) =$

   b. $P(\ ☀\ ) =$

   c. $P(\ ☆\ ) =$

3. Jonah makes the following predictions for the spinner landing on each symbol. Do you think his predictions are correct?

$$P(☺) = \frac{1}{4} \qquad P(☀) = \frac{1}{4} \qquad P(☆) = \frac{2}{5}$$

4. Is there a way to determine the exact probabilities of landing on each of the shapes? Explain your reasoning.

Let's determine the experimental probability of the spinner landing on each of the symbols. Use a paper clip as the arrow part of the spinner. Place a pencil point through the paper clip, and then on the center of the circle. Working with a partner, one person w spin the spinner and the other person will record the result of each spin.

5. Spin the spinner 50 times and record the data using tally marks. Then, complete the table.

Shape	Tally	Total	Probability
☺			
☀			
☆			

6. Calculate the experimental probabilities using your data.

   a. $P(☺) =$

   b. $P(☀) =$

   c. $P(☆) =$

7. Compare the experimental probabilities with your predictions from Question 2. What do you notice? Why did this happen?

8. Compare your experimental probabilities with your classmates. What do you notice?

If you know an event's probability of occurring, then you can make predictions of the event occurring for the number of times an experiment is conducted. To make this prediction, you can use proportional reasoning.

The probability that a spinner will land on ✷ is $\frac{7}{20}$.

If you spin the spinner 60 times, you can predict the number of times the spinner will land on the ✷ section.

Step 1: Set up a proportion.

$$\frac{\text{number of times an event will occur}}{\text{number of possible outcomes}} \qquad \frac{7}{20} = \frac{x}{60}$$

You know that $P(✷) = \frac{7}{20}$. You also know that you are going to spin the spinner 60 times.

Step 2: Solve the proportion.

$$\frac{7}{20} = \frac{x}{60}$$
$$420 = 20x$$
$$\frac{420}{20} = \frac{20x}{20}$$
$$21 = x$$

If you spin the spinner 60 times, you can expect it to land on the ✷ 21 times.

9. Suppose the probabilities for the symbols on the spinner are known to be:

$P($$) = \frac{7}{20}$ $\qquad$ $P($$) = \frac{2}{5}$ $\qquad$ $P($$) = \frac{1}{4}$

a. If you spin the spinner 40 times, predict the number of times the spinner would land on each symbol:

 : : :

b. If you spin the spinner 100 times, predict the number of times you would land on each symbol:

 : : :

c. How did you predict the number of times the spinner would land on each symbol for the given number of times the spinner would be spun?

d. In parts (a) and (b), do you think you would land on the symbol exactly the number of times you calculated if you spin the spinner? Why or why not?

Problem 3 Even I Win, Odd You Win...

Joel and Hiram are playing a game using 2 six-sided number cubes. The number cubes are rolled, and the sum of the 2 numbers shown is calculated. If the sum is even, Joel wins a point. If the sum is odd, Hiram wins a point.

1. List the sample space for the game.

2. Do you think each of the outcomes is equally likely? Explain your reasoning.

Time to make your predictions.

3. Who do you think has a better chance of winning this game? Explain your reasoning.

4. Play the game 25 times with a partner. Record your sums in the table.

Sum of Two Number Cubes	Tally Mark
2	
3	
4	
5	
6	
7	

Sum of Two Number Cubes	Tally Mark
8	
9	
10	
11	
12	

5. According to your experiment, who would win the game between Joel and Hiram?

6. Calculate the experimental probability for each outcome. Express your probability as a fraction and a percent.

a. $P(2) = $ _____

b. $P(3) = $ _____

c. $P(4) = $ _____

d. $P(5) = $ _____

e. $P(6) = $ _____

f. $P(7) = $ _____

g. $P(8) = $ _____

h. $P(9) = $ _____

i. $P(10) = $ _____

j. $P(11) = $ _____

k. $P(12) = $ _____

7. How might you calculate the actual probability for each outcome?

8. Make a list of all of the possible outcomes when rolling 2 six-sided number cubes.

How can you organize your list to make sure you get all the possibilities?

9. How many different possibilities are there when rolling 2 six-sided number cubes?

10. Does the experimental probability of the game seem to match your prediction of the winner? Explain your reasoning.

11. Do you think that each number that can be rolled with two number cubes have an equally likely chance of occurring? Do you think it can affect the result of the game?

Be prepared to share your solutions and methods.

DOUBLE YOUR FUN

16.3

Determining Theoretical Probability

Learning Goals

In this lesson, you will:

▶ Calculate the experimental and theoretical probability of an experiment.

▶ Determine the difference between experimental and theoretical probability.

▶ Use proportional reasoning to predict probability of random events.

Key Term

▶ theoretical probability

There are three doors. Behind one of the doors is a prize. Behind the other two doors are donkeys. You choose one door. The game show host opens one of the doors that you did *not* choose to reveal a donkey. Then, the host asks you if you would like to stay on the door you chose or switch to the other unopened door. Should you stay or switch? Or does it matter?

This famous probability problem is known as the Monty Hall problem—named after the host of the game show *Let's Make a Deal*, which featured this problem.

Surprisingly, the answer is that you should switch! When you switch you have a $\frac{2}{3}$ chance of getting the prize. If you stay, you have only a $\frac{1}{3}$ chance.

Can you figure out why you should switch every time? What if you had 100 doors to choose from and after you made your choice, the game show host opened 98 doors to reveal 98 donkeys?

Problem 1 Double Your Fun—Again!

Previously, Joel and Hiram were playing a game using 2 six-sided number cubes. The number cubes were rolled, and the sum of the 2 numbers shown was calculated. If the sum was even, Joel won a point. If the sum was odd, Hiram won a point. The experiment probability (the ratio of the number of times an event occurs to the total number of trials performed) was then calculated.

When you calculate the actual probability of an event before performing the experiment, you are determining the *theoretical probability*. **Theoretical probability** is the mathematical calculation that an event will happen in theory. The formula for theoretical probability is the ratio of the number of desired outcomes to the total number of possible outcomes, or the sample space.

$$\text{Theoretical Probability} = \frac{\text{number of desired outcomes}}{\text{total number of possible outcomes}}$$

1. List the sample space for the game played by Joel and Hiram.

In the previous experiment of rolling 2 six-sided number cubes, each of the outcomes in the sample space is not equally likely. One method to determine the probabilities of the outcomes is to make a list of all the possibilities.

For example, (1, 1) could represent rolling a 1 on the first number cube and a 1 on the second number cube. Another example, (1, 2) could represent rolling a 1 on the first number cube and a 2 on the second number cube.

The list shown lists all the possibilities when rolling 2 six-sided number cubes.

$$
\begin{aligned}
&(1, 1), (1, 2), (1, 3), (1, 4), (1, 5), (1, 6),\\
&(2, 1), (2, 2), (2, 3), (2, 4), (2, 5), (2, 6),\\
&(3, 1), (3, 2), (3, 3), (3, 4), (3, 5), (3, 6),\\
&(4, 1), (4, 2), (4, 3), (4, 4), (4, 5), (4, 6),\\
&(5, 1), (5, 2), (5, 3), (5, 4), (5, 5), (5, 6),\\
&(6, 1), (6, 2), (6, 3), (6, 4), (6, 5), (6, 6)
\end{aligned}
$$

2. How many different possibilities are there when rolling 2 six-sided number cubes?

Making a list can sometimes take a lot of time. Another way to determine all of the possibilities is to use a number array.

3. The array shown has two numbers filled in: 2 and 7. What does the 2 mean in the array? What does the 7 mean in the array?

Number Cube 1		1	2	3	4	5	6
Number Cube 2	1	2					
	2						
	3						
	4			7			
	5						
	6						

4. Complete the number array shown.

5. How many different possibilities are in the number array?

6. Does it appear that the list of all the possibilities when rolling 2 six-sided number cubes has the same number of possibilities as the number array?

7. Using the number array, determine the number of times each sum appears.

   a. sum of 2 _____

   b. sum of 3 _____

   c. sum of 4 _____

   d. sum of 5 _____

   e. sum of 6 _____

   f. sum of 7 _____

   g. sum of 8 _____

   h. sum of 9 _____

   i. sum of 10 _____

   j. sum of 11 _____

   k. sum of 12 _____

8. Calculate the theoretical probabilities for each sum.

   a. $P(2) = $ _____

   b. $P(3) = $ _____

   c. $P(4) = $ _____

   d. $P(5) = $ _____

   e. $P(6) = $ _____

   f. $P(7) = $ _____

   g. $P(8) = $ _____

   h. $P(9) = $ _____

   i. $P(10) = $ _____

   j. $P(11) = $ _____

   k. $P(12) = $ _____

9. Is there an equally likely chance for each number to result from rolling 2 six-sided number cubes according to the theoretical probabilities?

10. According to the theoretical probabilities, who should win the game? Explain your reasoning.

11. Did the experimental probability of your experiment in the previous lesson match the theoretical probability of the game? If not, why do you think the results of the experimental and theoretical probabilities were different?

12. Calculate each probability when rolling 2 six-sided number cubes using your number array. Explain your calculations.

    a. *P*(same number shows on each number cube)

    b. *P*(sum of the roll is a prime number)

    c. *P*(sum of the roll is greater than 7)

Remember, when you know an event's probability of occurring, use proportional reasoning to help you predict how often the event may occur for the number of trials the experiment is conducted!

    d. *P*(sum of the roll is 1)

13. If the number cubes are tossed 180 times, how many times do you predict the following sums would occur?

    a. 1   **b.** 4   **c.** 9

d. 10   **e.** 12   **f.** prime number

16

14. Kelsey claims that getting a sum of 4 when rolling two number cubes should be 1 ou of 11 since there are 11 possible outcomes. Do you agree with Kelsey's claim? If no how could you convince Kelsey that her thinking is incorrect?

Problem 2   Square Spinners Revisited

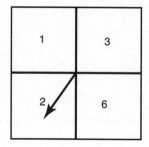

The square spinner shown is spun twice, and the results of the two spins are multiplied together to produce a product that is recorded.

1. Determine all the possibilities for obtaining the products using a list.

2. List the sample space.

3. Are all outcomes equally likely? Explain your calculations.

4. Complete the number array shown to validate your calculations.

Spin 1				
Spin 2				

5. Calculate the probability of each product.

a. $P(1)$ _____

b. $P(2)$ _____

c. $P(3)$ _____

d. $P(4)$ _____

e. $P(6)$ _____

f. $P(9)$ _____

g. $P(12)$ _____

h. $P(18)$ _____

i. $P(36)$ _____

6. Did you calculate the experimental or theoretical probability? Explain how you know.

7. Calculate each probability shown for the square spinner.

    a. *P*(spin results in an even product)

    b. *P*(spin results in an odd product)

Remember, a perfect square is the product of a factor multiplied by itself!

    c. *P*(spin results in a multiple of 3)

    d. *P*(spin results in a perfect square)

    e. *P*(spin results in a product is less than 50)

8. If the spinner is spun 200 times, how many times do you predict you would get each product:

    a. 2   **b.** 3

    c. 6   **d.** 36

e. an even product   **f.** an odd product

Talk the Talk

16

1. Explain the difference between experimental and theoretical probability.

2. Determine if each probability of the scenario can be calculated experimentally, theoretically, or both. Explain your reasoning.

   a. The probability of the spinner landing on red.

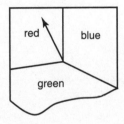

A four-sided polyhedron is like a six-sided number cube. It's just that it has four sides instead of six! What do you think a four-sided polyhedron looks like?

b. P(sum of 4) when a four-sided number polyhedron with numbers 1 through 4 is rolled twice.

c. Probability a particular medicine will cure a disease.

d. Probability a bridge will collapse given the bridge's dimensions and appropriate mathematical formulas.

Be prepared to share your solutions and methods.

16.4

A TOSS OF A COIN
Simulating Experiments

Learning Goals

In this lesson, you will:

▶ Conduct trials using a simulation to determine probability.

▶ Conduct a large number of trials to demonstrate that experimental probability approaches theoretical probability.

Key Terms

▶ simulation

▶ trial

Are you an honest person? Do you have integrity? Do you do what is right even though there may not be laws telling you to do so? If yes, you may be described as having probity. Talking about a person's probity can be a way to gauge how reliable their testimony may be in court.

Did you know that the word "probability" comes from the word "probity"? How are these terms related? What are the similarities and differences in their meanings?

What percent of babies born at a hospital are girls? One way to answer the question is to perform a *simulation*. A **simulation** is an experiment that models a real-life situation. When conducting a simulation, you must choose a model that has the same probability of the event.

1. What model might be appropriate for doing a simulation?

2. Describe the sample space for this situation.

3. What is the event you are trying to determine?

4. Suppose the probability of a family having a girl is $\frac{1}{2}$.

   What percent of babies born at a hospital would you expect to be girls?

Let's use the toss of a coin as the model. Heads will represent the birth of a girl, and tails will represent the birth of a boy.

5. If you toss a coin twice, list all the possible outcomes from this simulation.

6. Toss your coin 2 times.

   a. How many of the coin tosses resulted in heads?

   b. According to your simulation, what is the experimental probability of a baby girl being born?

c. Share your results with your classmates. Then, create a dot plot of all the experimental probabilities from your and your classmates' simulations. Did everyone end up with the same results of the theoretical probability of a girl being born?

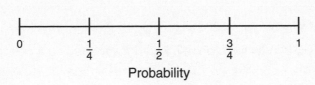

Probability

7. Toss your coin 4 times.

    a. How many of the coin tosses resulted in heads?

    b. According to your simulation, what is the experimental probability of a baby girl being born?

    c. Share your results with your classmates. Then, create a dot plot of all the experimental probabilities from your and your classmates' simulations. How do these results compare to the results from Question 6?

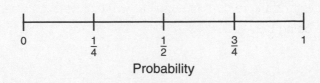

Probability

8. Toss your coin 8 times.

    a. How many of the coin tosses resulted in heads?

    b. According to your simulation, what is the experimental probability of a baby girl being born?

    c. Share your results with your classmates. Then, create a dot plot of all the experimental probabilities from your and your classmates' simulations. How do these results compare to the results from Questions 6 and 7?

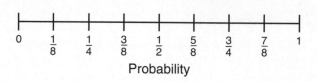

Probability

Each time you repeat an experiment or simulation, it is called a **trial**.

9. Conduct 50 trials of the simulation. Record the results in the table using tally marks.

Result	Tally	Total	Percent (total/50)
Heads			
Tails			

10. Share your results with your classmates. Then, create a dot plot of all the probabilities. What do you notice?

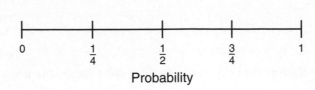

Probability

11. What can you conclude about the experimental probability of an event and its theoretical probability as the number of trials of the simulation increase?

You have demonstrated that the experimental probability of an event approaches the theoretical probability when the number of trials becomes greater. This fact is very useful in determining the probability of an event for which the experimental probability is difficult, or impossible, to calculate.

Problem 2   Test Guessing

Mr. Garcia, your history teacher, is giving a five-question multiple-choice test. Each question has 4 possible answers. How many questions can you expect to get correct simply by guessing?

Of course, if you know the answer, you don't have to guess. This is just an experiment and you should probably study so that you don't have to guess!

1. Estimate the number of questions you expect to get correct by guessing.

One model that you could use to simulate this problem situation is a spinner divided into 4 sections that are the same size.

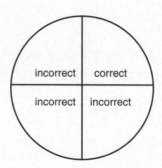

incorrect | correct
incorrect | incorrect

2. According to the spinner shown, what is the probability of correctly guessing the answer to one question?

3. Describe one trial of the experiment if you want to simulate guessing on every question of the test.

4. Will one trial provide a good estimate of how many questions you should expect to get correct? Explain your reasoning.

5. Conduct 50 trials of the simulation. Record your results in the table.

Trial Number	Number Correct	Trial Number	Number Correct	Trial Number	Number Correct
1		18		36	
2		19		37	
3		20		38	
4		21		39	
5		22		40	
6		23		41	
7		24		42	
8		25		43	
9		27		44	
10		28		45	
11		29		46	
12		30		47	
13		31		48	
14		32		49	
15		33		50	
16		34			
17		35			

6. Graph your results on the dot plot.

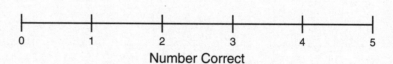

Number Correct

7. According to your simulation, about how many questions would you expect to get correct on the test by only guessing?

8. Do you think purely guessing on a five question multiple-choice test will result in a good grade on the test?

Describe a simulation to model each situation, and then describe one trial. Conduct the simulation and answer the question.

1. How many questions would you get correct on a 10-question true/false test simply by guessing?

   Simulation:

   Trial:

   Conduct the simulation one time:

2. The game of MATHO requires you to roll a 6 on a number cube before you can begin playing. How many times would you expect to roll the cube before you can begin the game?

   Simulation:

   Trial:

   Conduct the simulation 10 times and calculate the mean of your answers:

3. Stefan claims he can read your mind. He gives you four cards: a red 1, a blue 2, a blue 3, and a red 4. You draw one of the cards and look at it without showing Stefan

    a. If you ask Stefan to guess the color, what percent of the time could he guess correctly?

    Simulation:

    Trial:

    Conduct the simulation 10 times and count the number of times your card is selected:

    b. If you ask Stefan to guess the number, what percent of the time should he guess correctly?

    Simulation:

    Trial:

    Conduct the simulation 10 times and count the number of times your card is selected:

 Be prepared to share your solutions and methods.

16.5

ROLL THE CUBES AGAIN
Using Technology for Simulations

Learning Goal

In this lesson, you will:

▶ Use technology to simulate a large number of trials of an experiment.

Key Term

▶ spreadsheet

There are many different kinds of programs that generate what you might call "random numbers." But how can these programs do this? In order to generate random numbers, some kind of code is needed to tell the computer what to produce. But if a code exists, then the numbers can't truly be random. In fact, most programs generate what are called "pseudo-random numbers." These are numbers that are not random at all, but are generated to appear random. Only in 2010 was a program developed to produce truly random numbers. How is randomness important in probability?

Recall Joel and Hiram were playing a game using 2 six-sided number cubes. The two number cubes were rolled and the sum of the two numbers was calculated.

1. Suppose you ran a simulation of this game as an experiment. How many times shou̲ you run the simulation to get a good idea of the probabilities of each sum?

One way to simulate the experiment is to actually roll the number cubes. Another way to simulate the experiment is to use a *spreadsheet*. A **spreadsheet** is a computer documen̲ that allows you to organize information in rows and columns. Computer spreadsheets typically have a number of tools such as mathematical formulas and functions that make easy to simulate experiments and analyze information.

A blank spreadsheet is shown. Notice that the columns are labeled with capital letters an̲ the rows are named with numbers beginning with the number 1. Each box is called a cell and can be named according to its row and column. For example, the highlighted cell is named F4.

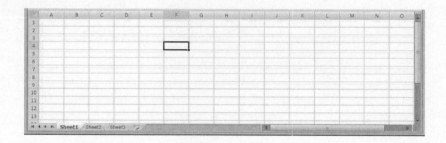

You can use a mathematical formula in a spreadsheet to simulate rolling number cubes. The mathematical function "RANDBETWEEN" will produce a random integer between an̲ including two given values.

2. What two numbers will you use in the function RANDBETWEEN to produce a random̲ integer to simulate rolling 1 six-sided number cube?

Typically, when working with a spreadsheet, you begin with the cell in the first row and first column.

3. What is the name of this cell?

Select a cell by clicking inside of it.

You always enter a formula in a spreadsheet by beginning with an "=" so that the program knows it is a formula and not just a word or a number.

Formulas are entered in the function area.

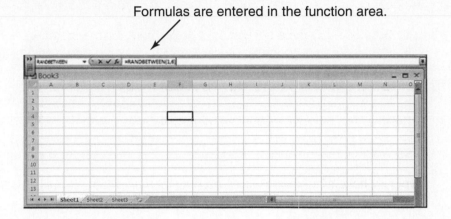

4. Enter the formula =RANDBETWEEN(1, 6) in the function area.

5. Press ENTER. What do you notice?

If you want to simulate rolling the number cube 10 times, you can type the formula in 10 cells, or use the "Fill" function. The "Fill" function pastes the same formula in all of the cells you select.

The "Fill" function is indicated by a down arrow next to the word "Fill" on the upper right side of the spreadsheet. Select cells A1 through A10. Then, click on the arrow next to "Fill" and select "Down."

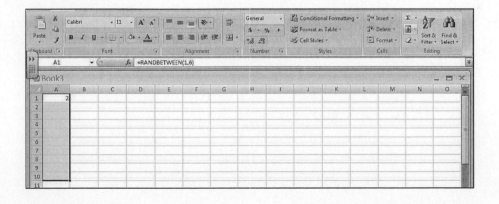

6. What do you notice?

Now let's simulate the game Joel and Hiram were playing.

7. What are the possible outcomes for each roll?

8. Are all of the outcomes equally likely? Explain your reasoning.

9. Would it make sense to choose random numbers from 2 through 12? Why or why not?

10. How can you simulate rolling two number cubes and calculating the sum?

One way to simulate rolling two number cubes and calculating the sum would be to enter a set of random integers from 1 through 6 into column A and another set into column B. You can then write a formula in column C to add columns A and B. Another approach would be to write a formula to add two random numbers from 1 through 6 together to get a sum.

11. Clear your current spreadsheet or open a new spreadsheet.
Enter the formula =RANDBETWEEN(1, 6) + RANDBETWEEN(1, 6) into cell A1 and press ENTER. What do you notice?

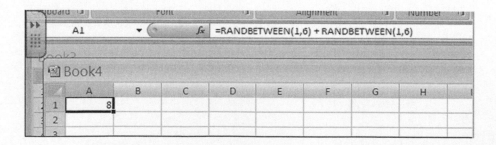

12. How could you simulate 10 trials?

13. Simulate 10 trials. Then, record your results in the table shown.

Result	Tally	Total	Probability (decimal)
2			
3			
4			
5			
6			
7			
8			
9			
10			
11			
12			
Total	10	10	1

14. Represent the results of your simulation by completing the bar graph with the resul

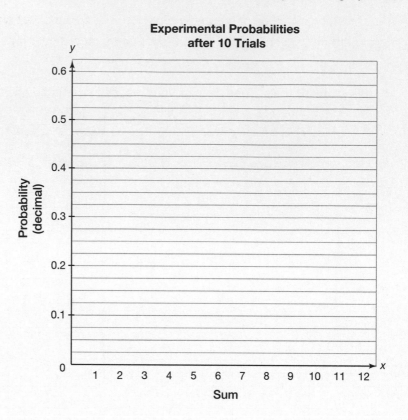

Experimental Probabilities after 10 Trials

15. Why must the last column of the table show a total of 1?

16. Do you think that performing 10 trials provides a good idea about the probability of each sum? Why or why not?

With a computer spreadsheet, it is easy to conduct hundreds or thousands of trials very quickly.

17. Conduct 100 trials of the experiment using a spreadsheet and the steps you learned to create simulations of experiments. Then, record your results in the table and in a bar graph.

Result	Tally	Total	Probability (decimal)
2			
3			
4			
5			
6			
7			
8			
9			
10			
11			
12			
Total	100	100	1

Experimental Probabilities
after 100 Trials

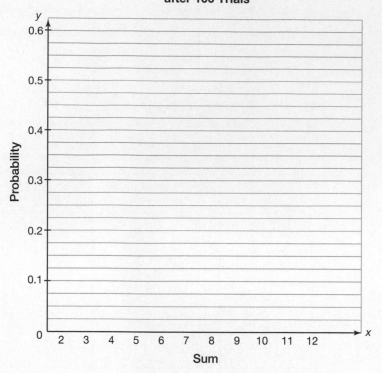

18. The theoretical probabilities of each sum are shown. Construct a bar graph of the theoretical probabilities shown in the table.

Sum	Probability	Sum	Probability
2	$\frac{1}{36} = 0.02\overline{7}$	8	$\frac{5}{36} = 0.13\overline{8}$
3	$\frac{2}{36} = 0.0\overline{5}$	9	$\frac{4}{36} = 0.\overline{11}$
4	$\frac{3}{36} = 0.08\overline{3}$	10	$\frac{3}{36} = 0.08\overline{3}$
5	$\frac{4}{36} = 0.\overline{11}$	11	$\frac{2}{36} = 0.0\overline{5}$
6	$\frac{5}{36} = 0.13\overline{8}$	12	$\frac{1}{36} = 0.02\overline{7}$
7	$\frac{6}{36} = 0.1\overline{6}$	Total	1

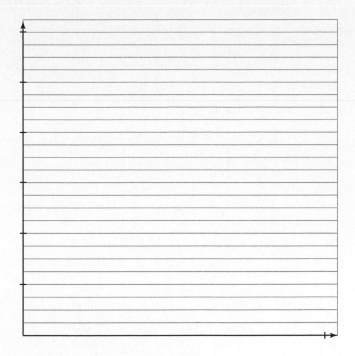

19. Compare the two bar graphs. What do you notice? Do you think the 100 trials of this experiment provided a good idea about the theoretical probabilities?

Problem 2   Retest

Design and carry out a simulation for the five-question test guessing experiment using a computer spreadsheet. Recall that each question had 4 answer choices, but only one choice is the correct answer.

1. If there are 4 possible answers for each question, how many random numbers do you need for each question?

2. Describe one trial.

Since there are 5 questions on the test, use 5 columns in the first row to simulate one trial of guessing on the test. Type the formula =RANDBETWEEN(1, 4) in cell A1 and fill RIGHT to cell E1. Let the number 1 represent a correct guess and numbers 2, 3, and 4 represent incorrect guesses.

3. List and interpret the results of your first trial.

4. Highlight the first row, and then fill down through row 25. What does filling down through row 25 represent?

5. Record your results in the table shown.

Trial Number	Number Correct
1	
2	
3	
4	
5	
6	
7	
8	
9	
10	
11	
12	
13	

Trial Number	Number Correct
14	
15	
16	
17	
18	
19	
20	
21	
22	
23	
24	
25	

6. Represent the results in your table on the dot plot shown.

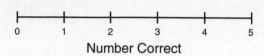

Number Correct

7. What is the experimental probability of guessing:

    a. 0 questions correctly?

    b. 1 question correctly?

    c. 2 questions correctly?

    d. 3 questions correctly?

    e. 4 questions correctly?

    f. all 5 questions correctly?

8. Would you advise your friends to guess on this multiple-choice test? Why or why not

Lauren has a two-point shooting average of 70%. Katie has a three-point shooting average of 60%.

If Lauren takes 4 two-point shots, and Katie takes 4 three-point shots, how many points would they be expected to score?

1. Predict the number of points each girl will score.

In addition to computer spreadsheets, you can also use graphing calculators to simulate trials of an experiment. A graphing calculator also allows you to generate random integers between two numbers.

2. What might be a good model to use for this problem situation?

3. If you generate random numbers from 1 through 10, how can you tell whether or not Lauren made her shot?

4. Why would you use 10 random numbers for the simulation?

5. Describe one trial of this simulation.

16

Let's say that the numbers 1 through 7 represent Lauren making a two-point shot and th
numbers 8 through 10 represent Lauren missing the shot.

Follow the steps to generate random integers using a graphing calculator.

Step 1: Press ⬛MATH and use the right arrow to move the cursor to ⬛PRB.

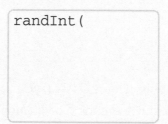

```
MATH NUM CPX PRB
1:rand
2:nPr
3:nCr
4:!
5:randInt(
6:randNorm(
7:randBin(
```

Step 2: Use the down arrow to highlight **5: randInt(** and press ⬛ENTER.

```
randInt(
```

Step 3: Enter the number ⬛1 followed by a ⬛, and the number ⬛10 and press ⬛ENTER.
random number between 1 and 10 should appear.

```
randInt(1,10
                    6
■
```

6. According to the screen shot shown, did Lauren make the two-point shot? Explain
your reasoning.

If you want to simulate Lauren shooting 4 times, you can continue to press ENTER until you have 4 random numbers. You can also tell the calculator to generate 4 numbers at a time.

Step 1: Press MATH and use the right arrow to move the cursor to PRB .

Step 2: Use the down arrow to highlight 5: **randInt(** and press ENTER .

Step 3: Enter the number 1 , a , , the number 10 , a , , and the number 4 . Press ENTER .

Four random numbers between 1 and 10 should appear.

```
randInt(1,10,4
        (8 9 3 3)
```

7. According to the screen shot shown, how many two-point baskets did Lauren make? Explain your reasoning.

8. According to the simulation, if Lauren attempted four shots, how many points would she score?

Let's simulate this experiment 25 times.

9. Why should you simulate the experiment 25 times rather than 1 time or 5 times?

10. Simulate the experiment of Lauren shooting 4 shots 25 times. Record your results in the table.

16

Trial Number	Result	Number of Shots Made	Total Points Made
1			
2			
3			
4			
5			
6			
7			
8			
9			
10			
11			
12			
13			
14			
15			

Trial Number	Result	Number of Shots Made	Total Points Made
16			
17			
18			
19			
20			
21			
22			
23			
24			
25			
	TOTAL		

16

11. Plot your results for the number of points Lauren scored from the simulation on the dot plot. Then, make a prediction about how many points Lauren would be expecte to make if she attempted 4 shots. Explain your reasoning.

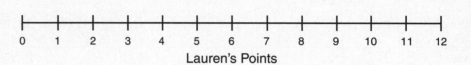

Lauren's Points

12. Use the results from the table in Question 10 to answer each.

    a. Calculate the mean number of times Lauren would be expected to score if she attempted 4 shots. Then, convert your answer to a percent. Does your answer make sense? Why or why not?

How do you think you would calculate the mean from the simulations you conducted? Do you think your mean will be more or less than I?

16

    b. Calculate the mean number of points Lauren would be expected to make if she attempted four shots. How does the answer compare to your prediction?

13. Repeat the simulation for Katie.

  a. What would you need to change in the simulation?

  b. Simulate the experiment of Katie shooting 4 shots 25 times. Record your results.

Trial Number	Result	Number of Shots Made	Total Points Made
1			
2			
3			
4			
5			
6			
7			
8			
9			
10			
11			
12			
13			
14			
15			

Trial Number	Result	Number of Shots Made	Total Points Made
16			
17			
18			
19			
20			
21			
22			
23			
24			
25			
	TOTAL		

16

14. Plot your results for the number of points Katie scored from the simulation on the d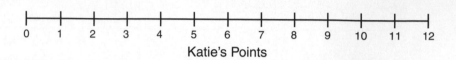 plot. Then, make a prediction about how many points Katie would be expected to score if she attempted four shots.

```
├──┼──┼──┼──┼──┼──┼──┼──┼──┼──┼──┼──┤
0   1   2   3   4   5   6   7   8   9   10  11  12
```
Katie's Points

15. Use the results from the table in Question 13 to answer each.

    a. Calculate the average number of times Katie would be expected to score if she attempted 4 shots. Then, convert your answer to a percent. Does your answer make sense? Why or why not?

    b. Calculate the average number of points Katie would be expected to make if she attempted four shots. How does the answer compare to your prediction?

16. Even though Lauren had a higher average number of shots made than Katie, why did Katie have a higher average number of points scored?

Problem 4   Probability Simulation

One advantage to simulating experiments on a graphing calculator rather than on a computer spreadsheet is that many graphing calculators have built-in probability simulations.

Follow the steps and run the Probability Simulation on a graphing calculator.

Step 1: Press the APPS key. A list of applications for the calculator should appear.

```
APPLICATIONS
1:Finance...
2:ALGICH5
3:ALGIPRT1
4:AreaForm
5:CabriJr
6:CelSheet
7↓Conics
```

Depending on your graphing calculator, you might have to scroll for a while! The applications are listed in alphabetical order!

Step 2: Use the down arrow to scroll down to: **Prob Sim**.

```
APPLICATIONS
↑OrganESP
:OrganFra
:Organize
:Perioden
:Periodic
:Prob Sim
↓PuzzPack
```

Step 3: Press ENTER twice.

```
Simulation
1.Toss Coins
2.Roll Dice
3.Pick Marbles
4.Spin Spinner
5.Draw Cards
6.Random Numbers
OK|   |OPTN|ABOUT|QUIT
```

Scroll down to **3. Pick Marbles** and press ENTER . The application allows you to select the number of marbles, how many marbles of each "color," and the number of trials.

Step 4: Press the ZOOM button.

Use the arrow keys to set the calculator to the following. Once a word or number is highlighted, you must press ENTER .

- Trial Set: **1**
- Types: **2** 3 4 5
- Graph: **Freq** Prob
- StoTbl: No **All** 50
- ClearTbl: **Yes**
- Replace: **Yes** No

Step 5: Press the WINDOW button.

Choose **7** Marble A and **3** Marble B.

Step 6: Press the GRAPH button below **OK** twice. You are now ready to begin the simulation.

Step 7: Press the WINDOW button below **PICK**.

Step 8: The calculator shows which marble was picked. The graph shows the frequency of each marble being picked. Use the arrow keys to scroll over the graph and the frequency of each marble will be shown.

Step 9: Press the WINDOW button below **+1**. This will result in another trial being conducted.

If you scroll over to the graph, the sum of the frequencies should now be 2.

Step 10: Press the ZOOM button below **+10**. This will result in 10 more trials being conducted.

If you scroll over to the graph, the sum of the frequencies should now be 12.

Step 11: Continue selecting marbles until you have conducted the desired number of trials.

roblem 5   I've Lost My Marbles!

With a partner, you will play the game "I've Lost My Marbles." You can either play Version A or B of this game. You will need your graphing calculator to play this game.

VERSION A

One person will set the calculator without the partner knowing the settings. The other partner will run the simulation and try to guess the number of marbles of each "color" in the bag.

Rules:

1. Use marbles of 2 different colors.

2. The sum of the number of marbles must be 10. (For example, Marble A: 6, Marble B: 4.)

3. One partner makes guesses in the table as to the number of each marble after the 1st, 5th, 10th, 20th, and 50th trials.

4. After the 50th trial, the other partner reveals how many of each marble were in the bag.

5. The partners switch roles and repeat the game. The partner who is the closest to guessing the correct number of each color marble wins.

Partner A	Guess	Partner B	Guess
1 trial		1 trial	
5 trials		5 trials	
10 trials		10 trials	
20 trials		20 trials	
50 trials		50 trials	

VERSION B

One person will set the calculator without the partner knowing the settings. The other partner will run the simulation and try to guess the number of marbles of each "color" in the bag.

Rules:

1. Use marbles of three different colors.

2. The sum of the number of marbles must be 10. (For example, Marble A: 5, Marble B 4, Marble C: 1.)

3. The partner makes guesses in the table as to the number of each marble after the 1st 5th, 10th, 20th, and 50th trials.

4. After the 50th trial, the other partner reveals how many of each marble were in the bag.

5. The partners switch roles and repeat the game. The partner who is the closest to guessing the correct number of each color marble wins.

Partner A	Guess	Partner B	Guess
1 trial		1 trial	
5 trials		5 trials	
10 trials		10 trials	
20 trials		20 trials	
50 trials		50 trials	

 Be prepared to share your solutions and methods.

16

Key Terms

- outcome (16.1)
- experiment (16.1)
- sample space (16.1)
- event (16.1)
- simple event (16.1)
- probability (16.1)
- equally likely (16.1)
- experimental probability (16.2)
- theoretical probability (16.3)
- simulation (16.4)
- trial (16.4)
- spreadsheet (16.5)

16.1 Determining Sample Space

The result of an experiment is an outcome. The list of all possible outcomes for an experiment is called a sample space. A sample space is typically enclosed in { } with commas between the outcomes.

Example

The sample space for an experiment spinning this spinner is {triangle, 6, 7, square, 4}.

16.1 Listing Outcomes for an Event

An event is either a single outcome in a sample space or a set of outcomes in the sample space. An outcome is the result of a single trial of an experiment.

Example

The spinner shown is spun one time. The outcomes for the event that the spinner landing on a shape are two because there are two shapes in the sample space: a triangle and a square.

16.1 Calculating the Probability of an Event

Probability is a measure of the likelihood that an event will occur. To calculate the probability of an event, determine the ratio of the number of times the event occurs to the total number of outcomes. The probability of an event is often noted as P(event).

Example

For the experiment of spinning the spinner one time, calculate the probability that the spinner lands on a number.

$$P(\text{number}) = \frac{\text{number of times a number occurs}}{\text{total number of outcomes}} = \frac{3}{5}$$

16.1 Estimating the Probability of an Event

The probability of an event can range from 0 (impossible) to 1 (certain). The more likely that the event is to occur, the closer the probability is to 1. An event with a probability of 0.5 or 50% is just as likely to occur as to not occur.

Example

The probability of the spinner landing on 2 is more than one-fourth of the circle, but less than half of the circle. A reasonable estimate for the probability would be between 30% and 35%.

16.1 Estimating the Probability of an Everyday Event

Be careful saying that a probability is 0 or 1. The probability of an everyday event that is unlikely to occur, but still possible, might best be estimated with a probability such as 0.000001.

Example

You can estimate the probability that it snows in the capital of Alaska on New Year's Eve. Because of its climate, it is very likely to snow in Alaska on a winter day. But it is not certain to happen. A reasonable estimate of the probability is 80%.

16

16.1 Calculating the Probability of an Everyday Event

Situations involving chance are not limited to number cubes and spinners. Everyday events can include games, weather, and even choosing apples.

Example

Sherri has 3 red delicious apples, 6 gala apples, and 5 golden delicious apples in a bag. She chooses one apple without looking. The probability of Sherri choosing a gala apple from the bag is shown.

$$P(\text{gala}) = \frac{\text{number of times she can choose a gala apple}}{\text{total number of apples}} = \frac{6}{14} = \frac{3}{7}$$

I don't know about you, but I can't wait until I graduate from high school!

16.2 Calculating an Experimental Probability

Every running of an experiment is called a trial. Experimental probability is based on several trials of the same experiment. For many experiments, a tally table is an easy way to track the results of trials. To calculate an experimental probability, determine the ratio c the number of times an event occurred in your experiment by the total number of trials yo performed for the experiment.

Experimental probabilities will vary. One day, you may roll an even number 14 times when rolling a number cube 20 times. The next day, you may roll an even number 11 times whe rolling the number cube 20 times.

Example

Lyle flipped a coin 10 times and recorded the data in the table shown. He then calculated the experimental probability of tossing heads and the experimental probability of tossing tails.

Lyle's Experimental Probability of Tossing a Coin 10 times

Result	Tally	Total
Heads	⊬⊬ ||	7
Tails	|||	3
		10

$$P(\text{heads}) = \frac{\text{number of times heads occurred}}{\text{number of trials}} = \frac{7}{10} = 70\%$$

$$P(\text{tails}) = \frac{\text{number of times tails occurred}}{\text{number of trials}} = \frac{3}{10} = 30\%$$

6.2 Using Proportional Reasoning to Predict the Probability of Random Events

When the probability of an outcome is known, you can set up a proportion to predict the number of times you can expect a certain outcome for a certain number of trials.

Example

Suppose the probabilities for the colors on a spinner are known to be:

$$P(\text{red}) = \frac{3}{8} \qquad\qquad P(\text{blue}) = \frac{1}{2} \qquad\qquad P(\text{yellow}) = \frac{1}{8}$$

If you spin the spinner 40 times, the number of times you would expect to land on each color are:

red:
$$\frac{x}{40} = \frac{3}{8}$$
$$8x = 120$$
$$x = 15 \text{ times}$$

blue:
$$\frac{x}{40} = \frac{1}{2}$$
$$2x = 40$$
$$x = 20 \text{ times}$$

yellow:
$$\frac{x}{40} = \frac{1}{8}$$
$$8x = 40$$
$$x = 5 \text{ times}$$

16.3 Determining the Type of Probability to Use in a Situation

Theoretical probability is calculated by creating a ratio of the favorable outcomes to the total number of outcomes. This number is based on what should happen mathematically. Sometimes it is not possible to determine a theoretical probability, and you can only determine an experimental probability.

$$\text{Theoretical Probability} = \frac{\text{number of desired outcomes}}{\text{total number of possible outcomes}}$$

Example

Determining if a bus stays on schedule could be determined by experimental probability.

Because there is no given outcomes to count, theoretical probability is impossible to calculate. You can track the number of times the bus is on schedule on a calendar and calculate the probability after a few weeks. Then, you can update the probability to include more trials every month or so.

16.3 Using a Number Array to Calculate a Theoretical Probability

It can become difficult to keep track of certain types of outcomes, particularly when combining results from two trials of an experiment. To organize the outcomes in a number array, list the outcomes for one trial along one side and the outcomes for the other trial along the other side of a number array. Combine the results in the intersections of each row and column.

Example

Vinnie spins this spinner 2 times and determines the sum of the two numbers.

		First Spin			
		2	**5**	**7**	**9**
Second Spin	**2**	4	7	9	11
	5	7	10	12	14
	7	9	12	14	16
	9	11	14	16	18

There are 16 possible outcomes, of which 6 are odd and 10 are even.

$P(\text{sum of the spins is an odd number}) = \dfrac{6}{16} = \dfrac{3}{8}$

6.4 Determining an Appropriate Model to Simulate an Experiment

A simulation is an experiment that models a real-life situation. When simulating an event, it is important to choose a model that has the same probability of the event you are simulating. Coins, spinners, or number cubes are models that can be used. The choice of which model should be used depends on the known probabilities of the events of a given situation.

Each performance of an experiment is a trial. The greater the number of trials, the closer the experimental probability will be to the theoretical probability.

Example

A test has 8 multiple-choice questions. Each question has 3 possible answers. You want to know the probability of getting at least four correct answers just by guessing.

For each question, there is one correct answer and two incorrect answers, so the probability of a correct answer is $\frac{1}{3}$. You can roll a number cube and let the numbers 1 and 2 represent correct answers and the numbers 3, 4, 5, and 6 represent incorrect answers. One trial is rolling the number cube 8 times (once for each question) and determining whether or not there are 4 or more correct answers.

16.4 Conducting a Simulation to Determine an Experimental Probability

Tables are a good way to track and record the results of simulations.

Example

Ten trials of the previous experiment are shown.

Trial Number	Number Correct	Trial Number	Number Correct
1	1	6	0
2	2	7	1
3	3	8	0
4	6	9	1
5	1	10	1

The experimental probability of getting at least 4 correct answers is 10% because only one of the 10 trials resulted in at least 4 correct answers.

16.5 Using a Spreadsheet to Perform a Simulation

A spreadsheet is a computer document that allows you to organize information in rows and columns. Many types of functions can be entered into a spreadsheet. For simulation an important function is RANDBETWEEN. It randomly chooses a number in the given range of numbers that you choose. Remember to put an equals sign before the command to indicate that you are writing a function.

Example

The probability that Julio will make a turn without falling while he is snowboarding down a hill is 60%. He will make 4 turns while going down the hill. You can use a spreadsheet to determine the experimental probability that Julio makes at least 3 turns without falling.

You can enter =RANDBETWEEN(1, 10) in cell A1 and copy it to the right through cell D1. This row represents one trial, or one time snowboarding downhill. Copy this row down through row 15 to simulate 15 trials. Let the numbers 1 through 6 represent a turn without falling (a successful turn) and the numbers 7 through 10 to represent a turn that results in falling.

Trial Number	Successful Turns	Trial Number	Successful Turns	Trial Number	Successful Turns
1	2	6	0	11	1
2	4	7	2	12	1
3	3	8	2	13	2
4	4	9	3	14	2
5	2	10	3	15	4

Of the 15 trials, six of them have at least three successful turns.

$$\frac{6}{15} = 40\%$$

The probability that Julio makes at least 3 turns without falling is 40%.

16.5 Using the Random Number Generator on a Graphing Calculator to Perform a Simulation

The randInt command on a graphing calculator randomly chooses an integer in the range of numbers that are provided to the calculator. To access the command, select MATH, arrow to PRB, and choose randInt. The first two numbers you type after the command determine the range of numbers the calculator can choose from. A third number is the number of random numbers you want to see at once. Continue to press ENTER to perform more trials of the same experiment.

Example

Tony makes a field goal 80% of the time. He attempts to make two field goals. Conduct 20 trials of an experiment to determine the experimental probability that he makes both goals.

Enter randInt (1, 10, 2) and press ENTER 20 times. Let the numbers 1 through 8 represent a successfully made field goal.

Trial Number	Results	Trial Number	Results	Trial Number	Results	Trial Number	Results
1	10, 5	6	3, 3	11	4, 4	16	5, 3
2	1, 1	7	10, 5	12	5, 9	17	3, 5
3	5, 8	8	8, 4	13	1, 3	18	2, 9
4	9, 1	9	7, 4	14	7, 8	19	2, 1
5	3, 5	10	6, 6	15	10, 1	20	8, 3

Of the 20 trials, 14 of them have two field goals (both numbers are 8 or less).

$$\frac{14}{20} = 70\%$$

The probability that Tony makes both field goals is 70%.

16.5 Using the Probability Simulation App on a Graphing Calculator

To access the Probability Simulation App, press the APPS key on a graphing calculator and scroll down to Prob Sim. There are 6 types of simulations. All work in a similar fashion by allowing you to set up the simulation as needed. You can show your results in a graph or table.

Example

The probability that Henrik performs a gymnastics routine without error is $\frac{1}{3}$.

The steps below describe how to use Pick Marbles and Spin Spinner to simulate his routine.

Pick Marbles: Choose two types of marbles. Let Type A represent a routine without error and Type B represent a routine with error. Set the number of Type A marbles to 1 and the number of Type B marbles to 2 to match the given probability.

Spin Spinner: Set the spinner so that there are three congruent sections. Let section 1 represent a routine without error and sections 2 and 3 represent a routine with error.

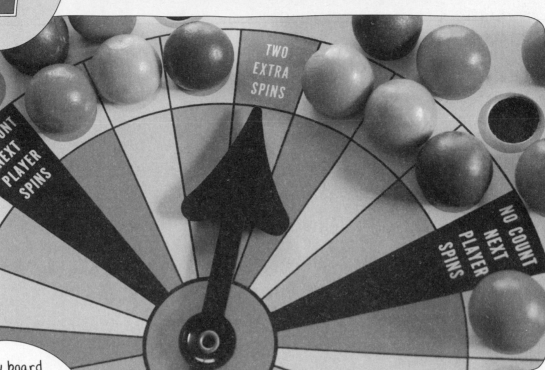

17 PROBABILITY OF COMPOUND EVENTS

Many board games use round spinners, number cubes, and numbered balls to drive game play. The size of the wedges on a spinner and the number on each ball determines the likelihood of a favorable result—and sometimes the likelihood of unfavorable results!

907

17

17.1

IS IT BETTER TO GUESS?

Using Models for Probability

Learning Goals

In this lesson, you will:

▶ Determine the probability model for an experiment.

▶ Construct and interpret a uniform probability model.

▶ Construct and interpret a non-uniform probability model.

Key Terms

▶ probability model

▶ uniform probability model

▶ non-uniform probability model

Have you ever encountered a test question, and you didn't know the answer? What did you do? Well, if the question was a multiple-choice question, did you guess which answer was correct?

While it is not always best to guess at the correct answer, there are some strategies to try to determine which answer choice is correct. One strategy is to try and determine the answer choices that are *not* realistic. For example, on a math test, if you are adding two positive integers, and one of the answer choices is a sum that is a negative integer, there is no possible way for that answer selection to be correct. So, you could eliminate that answer choice.

So, what strategies do you use when taking a test? Do you think it is better to guess the answer to a question if you don't know the answer?

Problem 1   Using Probability Models

Previously, you conducted trials for a simulation concerning guessing correct answers fo[r]
multiple-choice questions on a test. You will continue to explore the probability of
guessing on tests.

Jorge and Tristan are discussing the likelihood of correctly guessing the answer to a
multiple-choice question on a test if there were five choices for the answer choices instead
of four. They both assume that they have no idea what the correct answer is. They also
assume that each multiple-choice question has five possible answers: A, B, C, D, and E.

1. List the sample space for answering the multiple-choice question.

2. What is the theoretical probability if the correct answer is:

    A?   B?

    C?   D?

    E?

When solving a probability problem, it is helpful to construct a *probability model*.
A **probability model** is a list of each possible outcome along with its probability.
Previously, when you listed all the outcomes of an event or completed a
number array to show all outcomes of an event, you were using
a probability model. Probability models are often shown in a
table. The probability model for guessing the answer to a
multiple-choice question on a test is shown.

> Do you think
> a probability model
> represents experimental
> probability or theoretica[l]
> probability?

Outcome	A	B	C	D	E
Probability	0.2	0.2	0.2	0.2	0.2

3. What is the sum of the probabilities in the probability model?

As with the sum or probabilities, a probability model will list all the
outcomes which will be greater than 0, but less than 1. The sum of
all the probabilities for the outcomes will always be 1.

4. Why is the sum of the probabilities in a probability model always 1?

5. Tristan claims, "The model is also complete because the probabilities for all outcomes are equivalent to each other." Jorge disagrees and says, "The sum of all the probabilities is 1, but that does not mean the probability of each outcome is always equivalent to the other outcomes." Who is correct? Explain your reasoning.

A **uniform probability model** occurs when all the probabilities in a probability model are equally likely to occur. Assuming you do not know the answer to a five-choice multiple-choice question, each answer choice has the same probability of being correct. When all probabilities in a probability model are not equivalent to each other, it is called a **non-uniform probability model**. An example would be a weather forecast that states there is a 30 percent chance of rain. That means there is a 70 percent chance of *not* raining. The sum of these two probabilities is 1, but the outcomes do not have the same probability.

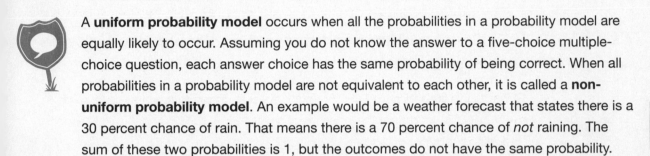

6. Suppose the correct answer to the multiple-choice question is C. Simulate answering the multiple-choice question by randomly selecting an answer choice 10 times. Write each answer choice on a piece of paper. Make sure all the pieces of paper are the same size. Record the number of times you draw the letter C which represents answering the question correctly.

7. Record your results and your classmates' results for the number of times the question was correctly answered on a dot plot.

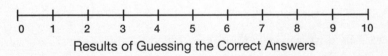

Results of Guessing the Correct Answers

8. According to the probability model, how many times should the correct answer have been guessed? Explain how you know.

9. Carla says that the probability model is incorrect since everyone in the class did not end up with 2 correct guesses as shown on the dot plot. Explain to Carla why the probability model is correct.

Problem 2   Constructing and Interpreting Probability Models

1. Construct a probability model for each situation. Explain how you constructed the model. Then, determine whether or not the probability model is a uniform probability model.

a. roll an 8-sided number polyhedron

Outcome								
Probability								

b. choose a marble from a bag of marbles containing 1 green marble, 2 red marbles, and 7 blue marbles

Outcome			
Probability			

An eight-sided polyhedron is like a six-sided number cube, but instead it has 8 sides. Do you think each side has the same probability as the other sides?

c. Randomly select a member of the Chess Club whose members are Samuel, Martha, Carol, Jon, Sally, Ronaldo, and Simon:

Outcome							
Probability							

d. Randomly select a male member of the Chess Club whose members are Samuel, Martha, Carol, Joanne, Sally, Ronaldo, and Simon:

Outcome		
Probability		

2. Use the probability model to calculate the probabilities:

Outcome	2	3	4	5	6	7
Probability	$\frac{1}{12}$	$\frac{3}{12}$	$\frac{1}{12}$	$\frac{5}{12}$	$\frac{1}{12}$	$\frac{1}{12}$

a. $P(3) =$

b. $P(8) =$

c. $P(\text{number less than 8}) =$

d. $P(\text{prime number}) =$

e. $P(\text{even number}) =$

17

1. The table shows how many students in Mr. York's homeroom have first names beginning with the letters listed.

Letter	Number of students
A	7
B	4
M	5
S	12
O	2

How many students are in Mr. York's homeroom?

2. Create a probability model for randomly selecting a student from Mr. York's homeroom.

17

3. What is the probability of randomly choosing a student with a first name that begins with a vowel?

4. What is the probability of randomly choosing a student with a first name that does no begin with S?

5. What is the probability of randomly choosing a student with a first name that begins with C?

Talk the Talk

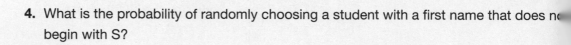

1. Do you think that you can use a probability model for both theoretical and experimental probability? Explain your reasoning.

2. What is the difference between a uniform probability model and a non-uniform probability model?

3. Will the sum of all the probabilities of the outcomes of an event be equal to 1 for both uniform and non-uniform probability models?

Be prepared to share your solutions and methods.

17.2

THREE GIRLS AND NO BOYS?

Creating and Using Probability Models

Learning Goals

In this lesson, you will:

▶ Determine the probability model for an experiment.

▶ Construct and interpret a non-uniform probability model.

Key Terms

▶ tree diagram

▶ complementary events

Do you think that there are the same number of girls and boys born each year? If you said yes, your answer would appear to make sense. Since there are really two choices of what a baby will be when he or she is born, there should be the same number of boys and girls born each year. However, that has not been the case in the United States. In fact, between 2000 and 2006, there have been 765,000 more baby boys born than baby girls. Do you think this trend might continue? Do you think this trend also occurs in other countries?

Problem 1   Constructing Probability Models

What is the probability that if a family has 3 children, those 3 children are girls?
Let's say that the theoretical probability of a girl being born is equal to the theoretical
probability of a boy being born, $\frac{1}{2}$.

Let's simulate the event of a family with 3 children having 3 girls.

1. What would be an appropriate model to simulate the probability of a family
    having one girl?

We will use 3 coin flips to simulate the event of a family having 3 girls. Let heads represent
a girl, and tails represent a boy.

A trial will consist of tossing a coin 3 times and counting the number of heads. Work with
partner—one person will toss the coin 3 times, and the other will record the results.

2. Conduct 25 trials of the simulation. Record the results in the table shown.

Trial	Number of Heads	Trial	Number of Heads	Trial	Number of Heads
1		10		19	
2		11		20	
3		12		21	
4		13		22	
5		14		23	
6		15		24	
7		16		25	
8		17			
9		18			

3. What are all the possible outcomes for the number of girls among 3 children?

4. Use the results from your simulation to construct a probability model.

Outcome	0 girls	1 girl	2 girls	3 girls
Probability				

5. What is the experimental probability that a family with 3 children has 3 girls according to your probability model?

In the above simulation your probability model is based on experimental probabilities. In some cases this is the only method of constructing a probability model. For example, you previously determined the experimental probabilities of a cup landing on its top, bottom, or side when it is tossed. It would be difficult or impossible to determine the theoretical probabilities for the cup toss. However, it is possible to determine the theoretical probability for a family with 3 children having 3 girls.

One method of determining the theoretical probability for a family having 3 girls is to list all of the possible outcomes for a family having 3 children, and then determining how many of those outcomes include 3 girls.

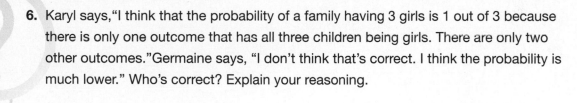

6. Karyl says, "I think that the probability of a family having 3 girls is 1 out of 3 because there is only one outcome that has all three children being girls. There are only two other outcomes." Germaine says, "I don't think that's correct. I think the probability is much lower." Who's correct? Explain your reasoning.

7. List all of the possible outcomes for having 3 children using G to represent girls, an̅ B to represent boys.

8. What does the outcome BGG represent?

9. Complete the probability model using all the possible outcomes.

Outcome	0 girls	1 girl	2 girls	3 girls
Probability				

10. What is the theoretical probability that a family having 3 children has 3 girls?

Another method of determining the theoretical probability of an event is to construct a tre̅ *diagram*. A **tree diagram** is a tree-shaped diagram that illustrates the possible outcomes of a given situation.

Examine the tree diagram showing all of the possible outcomes for a family having 3 children.

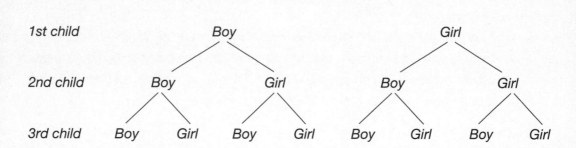

To determine each possible outcome from a tree diagram, you need to start with the first row of the tree diagram. Generally, this will be the top row, or the left-most row if the tree diagram is horizontal. Then, you need to move down each branch until you get to the final row.

For example, the first outcome listed would start with boy as the first child, then move down the branch to the second child which is a boy, and finally moving down the branch to the final row to the third child which is also a boy. So, this outcome would be BBB.

11. Explain the meaning of each entry in the "2nd child" row in each tree diagram.

12. Explain the meaning of each entry in the "3rd child" row.

13. How does the tree diagram compare to the list you made for Question 7?

14. Circle the outcome(s) of a family having three children that are all girls on the tree diagrams shown.

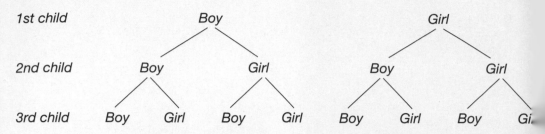

1st child   Boy   Girl

2nd child   Boy   Girl   Boy   Girl

3rd child   Boy   Girl   Boy   Girl   Boy   Girl   Boy   Gi...

15. Circle the outcome(s) of a family having three children in which two of the children ar... girls in the tree diagrams shown.

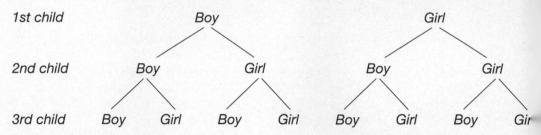

1st child   Boy   Girl

2nd child   Boy   Girl   Boy   Girl

3rd child   Boy   Girl   Boy   Girl   Boy   Girl   Boy   Gir...

16. Circle the outcome BBG in the tree diagrams shown.

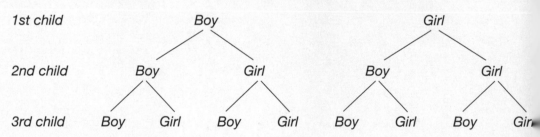

1st child   Boy   Girl

2nd child   Boy   Girl   Boy   Girl

3rd child   Boy   Girl   Boy   Girl   Boy   Girl   Boy   Gir...

17. Complete the probability model shown with the information from the tree diagrams.

Outcome	0 girls	1 girl	2 girls	3 girls
Probability				

18. Is there a difference in the theoretical probability of each outcome between the list of outcomes you wrote and the tree diagrams you analyzed?

The 5-sided spinner is spun twice and a product is calculated.

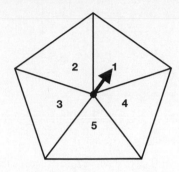

1. Use a tree diagram to determine all the possible outcomes. Then, list the product at the end of each branch of the tree.

2. Construct a probability model for spinning the spinner twice and recording the product.

Product	1	2	3	4	5	6	8
Probability							

Product	9	10	12	15	16	20	25
Probability							

3. Use the probability models you created to calculate the probability for each event shown.

a. *P*(product is 6)

b. *P*(product of 16)

c. *P*(product is less than 10)

d. *P*(product is a multiple of 5)

e. *P*(product is not a multiple of 5)

The events of the product being a multiple of 5 and the product not being a multiple of 5 are called *complementary events*. **Complementary events** are events that consist of the desired outcomes, and the remaining events that consist of all the undesired outcomes. Together, they include every possible outcome in the sample space.

4. Betina says that the product being less than 10 and the product being more than 10 are complementary events. Davika disagrees. Who is correct? Explain your reasoning.

5. What event would be complementary to the event that the product is an even number?

6. Determine P(product is an even number) and P(product is an odd number).

7. What is the sum of the probabilities of two complementary events? Explain why your answer makes sense.

Talk the Talk

1. Complete a tree diagram for all possible outcomes for correctly guessing the answers to a 3-question true-false quiz.

1st question

2nd question

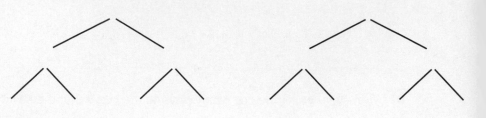

3rd question

2. Complete a probability model for the tree diagram you completed in Question 1.

Outcome	3 correct	2 correct	1 correct	0 correct
Probability				

3. Calculate the probabilities:

    a. *P*(all 3 questions correct) =

    b. *P*(1 or 2 questions correct) =

    c. *P*(0 questions are correct) =

Be prepared to share your solutions and methods.

17.3 PET SHOP PROBABILITY
Determining Compound Probability

Learning Goal

In this lesson, you will:

▶ Use probability models to calculate compound probabilities.

Key Term

▶ compound event

17

Have you ever heard the saying "Cats rule and dogs drool"? Or the saying "Dogs are a human's best friend"? It seems that people have been debating this question forever. It has even caused people to classify themselves as "cat people" or "dog people." The fact of the matter is that both animals are extremely popular and have been the center of many television shows. One show even tried to compare the good qualities of each animal to *prove* which animal was the better pet. In the end, the television program showed that dogs were just a little more popular. Do you have a cat or dog as a pet? Are you a cat person or a dog person?

Problem 1 I Want a Pet—But Which Type of Pet Do I Want?

Garden Plain Pet Shop has the following animals available for purchase. You will comple
a probability model and use it to determine the probability that the next pet chosen is a
dog or a cat.

Pets	Number Available
cat	4
dog	7
snake	1
rabbit	3
bird	5

1. How many pets are available for purchase?

2. Complete the probability model for purchasing a pet from Garden Plain Pet Shop.

Outcome	Cat	Dog	Snake	Rabbit	Bird
Probability					

3. Is the model a uniform or a non-uniform probability model? Explain your reasoning.

4. What is the probability the next pet purchased is:
   a. a dog?   b. a snake?   c. a cat?

5. What is the probability that the next pet purchased is a dog or a cat?

   a. How many of the pets are dogs or cats?

   b. How many total pets are there?

   c. What is the probability the next pet purchased is a dog or a cat?

Examples of students' methods in the Garden Plain math class to solve the Question 5 are shown.

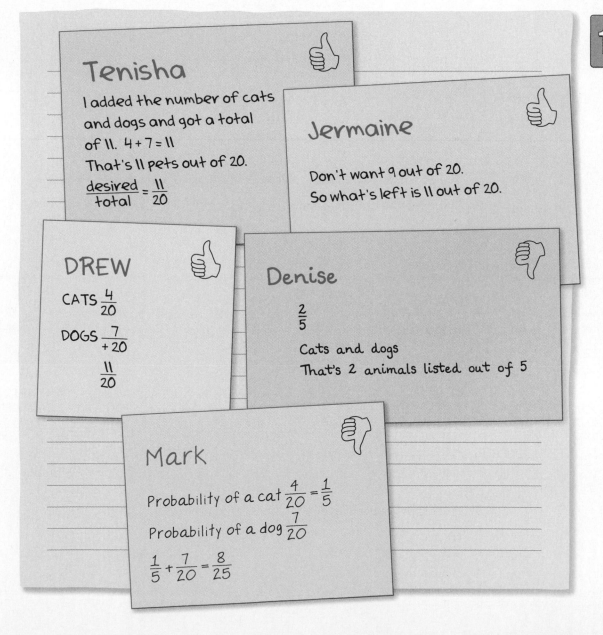

Tenisha 👍

I added the number of cats and dogs and got a total of 11. $4 + 7 = 11$

That's 11 pets out of 20.

$\dfrac{\text{desired}}{\text{total}} = \dfrac{11}{20}$

Jermaine 👍

Don't want 9 out of 20.
So what's left is 11 out of 20.

DREW 👍

CATS $\dfrac{4}{20}$

DOGS $\dfrac{7}{+20}$

$\dfrac{11}{20}$

Denise 👎

$\dfrac{2}{5}$

Cats and dogs
That's 2 animals listed out of 5

Mark 👎

Probability of a cat $\dfrac{4}{20} = \dfrac{1}{5}$

Probability of a dog $\dfrac{7}{20}$

$\dfrac{1}{5} + \dfrac{7}{20} = \dfrac{8}{25}$

6. Analyze each student's responses to the question.

    a. Describe the correct strategy Jermaine used.

    b. Describe the strategy Drew used.

    c. What is the difference between Tenisha's work and Drew's work?

    d. Explain to both Denise and Mark why their methods are incorrect for determining the probability the next pet purchased will be a cat or dog.

A **compound event** combines two or more events, using the word "and" or the word "or."

Determining the probability of a compound event with the word "and" is different from a compound event with "or."

The difference is that a compound event with the word "and" means that you are determining the probability for *one* event.

When determining a compound event with "or," you are determining the probability for more than one event. This is because either one event can occur *or* the other event can occur.

7. What is the probability the next pet purchased is a 4-legged animal?

   a. What events make up "the next pet purchased being a 4-legged animal"?

17

   b. How many event(s) are you determining the probability for? How do you know?

   c. Rewrite Question 7 using the events you wrote in part (a).

   d. Determine the probability the next pet purchased is a 4-legged animal. Show how you determined your answer.

Problem 2   Is It A Match?

1. The cards shown were placed face down in two piles so that they could be random
chosen. If one card is randomly chosen from each pile, what is the probability of
randomly choosing a matching pair?

   a. Determine the possible outcomes for randomly choosing one card from each pil
      Make sure you show your work by either creating an organized list or constructir
      a tree diagram.

17

   b. How many possible outcomes are there?

   c. What events make up randomly choosing a matching pair?

   d. Rewrite Question 1 using the events you wrote in part (c).

   e. Determine the probability of randomly choosing a pair.

2. Determine the probability of randomly choosing two cards that are a sum of 5. Show your work.

3. The class is asked to determine the probability of randomly choosing 2 odd cards. Lucy says, "The probability of drawing 2 odd cards is 3 out of 7 because there are 7 cards and 3 of them are odd." Do you agree with Lucy's statement? If not, explain to Lucy where her reasoning is not correct.

4. Write a problem using the number cards for which Lucy's answer would be correct:

5. What outcomes make up the event of choosing 2 odd cards given one card is chosen from each pile?

6. Determine the probability of randomly choosing 2 odd cards.

7. Determine the probability of selecting one card from each pile where the first card is a 2 and the second card is odd.

    a. List the event(s) for determining the probability.

    b. List the outcome(s) for the event(s).

    c. Determine the probability of selecting one card from each pile where the first card is a 2 and the second card is odd.

8. Determine the probability that the first card is a 2 or the second card is odd.

a. List the event(s) for determining the probability.

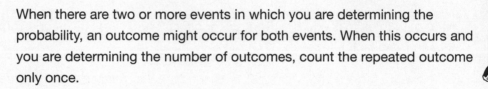

b. Determine the outcome(s) for the event(s).

c. How many outcomes are listed? Are any of the outcomes listed in both events?

When there are two or more events in which you are determining the probability, an outcome might occur for both events. When this occurs and you are determining the number of outcomes, count the repeated outcome only once.

d. How many different outcomes are there for the two events?

e. Determine the probability that the first card is a 2 or the second card is odd.

f. Why would we not count all the outcomes when calculating the probability?

9. Explain the difference between the events in Questions 7 and 8.

You and a friend are playing a game in which you take turns rolling a 6-sided number cube, and spinning a 4-number spinner.

You and your friend take turns.

- If your friend rolls an odd number and spins an even number, he or she wins.
- If you roll an even number and spin an odd number, you win.

1. List the possible outcomes for playing the game using a tree diagram.

2. Explain why the events of your friend winning or of you winning are compound events.

3. List the outcomes for the event of your friend winning the game.

4. What is the probability that your friend wins the game?

5. List the outcomes for the event of you winning the game.

6. What is the probability that you will win the game?

7. Do you and your friend have equally likely chances of winning the game? Explain your reasoning.

8. List the outcomes for and determine the probability for each statement.

    a. *P*(even number on the number cube and even number on the spinner)

b. *P*(even number on the number cube or even number on the spinner)

 Be prepared to share your solutions and methods.

17

WHAT TYPE OF BLOOD DO YOU HAVE?

Simulating Probability of Compound Events

17.4

Learning Goal

In this lesson, you will:

▶ Use simulations to estimate compound probabilities.

Do you know that there are four major blood groups: A, B, O, and AB. Did you know that the percent of people having each blood group differs by race and by country? For example, in some countries nearly everyone has the same blood group, and in other countries there are people who have each of the 4 blood groups. In the United States, the percent of people having each blood group differs by race and ethnicity. You may have noticed that there are often "blood drives" sponsored by the American Red Cross. These drives encourage people to donate blood that others can use if they are critically injured in accidents or natural disasters, or have serious diseases.

Problem 1   Blood Groups

Overall, the percent of people in the U.S. having each blood group is given in the table. The percents have been rounded to the nearest whole number percent.

Blood Groups	A	B	O	AB
Percent of Population	42%	10%	44%	4%

Suppose the Red Cross is having a blood drive at the Community Center.

1. What is the probability that the next person who enters the Community Center to donate blood has group A blood?

2. What is the probability that the next person who enters the Community Center to donate blood has group A or group O blood?

The first two questions involved events that the probability could be determined by using basic knowledge of probability. However, many events involve more advanced rules of probability. In most cases, though, a simulation can be used to model an event.

3. Determine the probability that out of the next 5 people to donate blood, at least 1 person has group AB blood.

   a. What could be a good model for simulating people who donate blood?

   b. You will use a random number table, a random digit generator on a calculator, or computer spreadsheet to model the problem. How could you assign numbers to people to account for the different blood types?

   c. Describe one trial of the simulation.

   d. Conduct 20 trials of the simulation and record your results in the table.

Trial Number	Numbers	Count of Numbers from 96 through 99
1		
2		
3		
4		
5		
6		
7		
8		
9		
10		
11		
12		
13		
14		
15		
16		
17		
18		
19		
20		

e. Out of the 20 trials, how many had at least 1 number from 96 through 99?

f. According to your simulation, what is the probability that out of the next 5 people to donate blood, at least one of them has type AB blood?

4. How many people would be expected to donate blood before a person with group B blood would donate blood?

   a. Describe one trial of the simulation.

   b. Conduct 20 trials of the simulation and record your results in the table.

Trial Number	Number of 2-digit numbers chosen until a number from 42 through 51 appears
1	
2	
3	
4	
5	
6	
7	
8	
9	
10	
11	
12	
13	
14	
15	
16	
17	
18	
19	
20	

17

c. Calculate the average for your 20 trials.

d. About how many people would be expected to donate blood before a person with group B blood enters?

Problem 2   Shoot Out

The star player on the basketball team typically makes 5 out of 6 free throws. There is a foul and the player gets to shoot 3 free throws.

1. What might be a good model for simulating the player shooting free throws?

2. How could you assign the numbers on the cube to model the player shooting free throws?

3. What is the probability that the player makes all 3 free throws?

   a. Describe one trial of the simulation.

   b. Conduct 20 trials of the simulation and record your results in the table.

Trial Number	Number of times a 1 through 5 occurs
1	
2	
3	
4	
5	
6	
7	
8	
9	
10	
11	
12	
13	
14	
15	
16	
17	
18	
19	
20	

17

c. Count the number of times that the result of all three numbers are between 1 and 5.

d. According to your simulation, what is the probability the player makes all 3 free throws?

4. Design and conduct a simulation to model the number of times the player would shoot before missing a shot.

Be prepared to share your solutions and methods.

17

Key Terms

▶ probability model (17.1)
▶ uniform probability model (17.1)
▶ non-uniform probability model (17.1)
▶ tree diagram (17.2)
▶ complementary events (17.2)
▶ compound event (17.3)

17.1

Constructing and Interpreting Probability Models

A probability model is a list of each possible outcome along with its probability. In a probability model, the probability of each outcome is greater than 0, but less than 1. The sum of the probabilities for all outcomes in a probability model will always be 1. When all of the probabilities in a probability model are equivalent to each other, it is called a uniform probability model. When all of the probabilities in a probability model are not equivalent, it is called a non-uniform probability model.

Example

Marshon spins a spinner with four equal sections on it as shown.

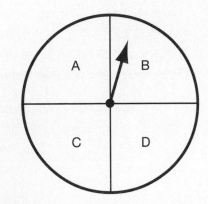

Think you are not good at math? As long as you work hard and have a good attitude you have a 100% chance of success!

17.1

The sample space for the spin is $S = \{A, B, C, D\}$. The probability of the spinner landing on one particular letter is $\frac{1}{4}$ or 0.25. The probability model for the situation is shown.

Outcome	A	B	C	D
Probability	0.25	0.25	0.25	0.25

The model is a uniform probability model because all of the probabilities in the model are equivalent to each other. The probability of spinning an A is $P(A) = 0.25$. To calculate the probability of not spinning a D, determine the sum of the probabilities of the other outcomes.

$$P(\text{not D}) = P(A) + P(B) + P(C)$$
$$= 0.25 + 0.25 + 0.25$$
$$= 0.75$$

The probability of not spinning a D is 0.75 out of 1.

17

17.2

Using Tree Diagrams to Determine Probabilities

One method of determining theoretical probability is to construct a tree diagram. A tree diagram is a tree-shaped diagram that illustrates sequentially the possible outcomes of a given situation. Complementary events are events that consist of the desired outcomes and the remaining events that consist of all the undesired outcomes. Together, they include every possible outcome in the sample space.

Example

Tina wants to determine the probability of spinning a four-number spinner twice and getting a sum of 6. She spins the spinner twice and records the sum of the two spins.

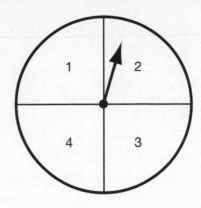

17.2

The tree diagram displays the possible outcomes of two spins.

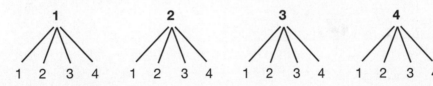

The probability model displays the probability of getting the possible sums with two spins.

Outcome (Sum of 2 spins)	2	3	4	5	6	7	8
Probability	$\frac{1}{16}$	$\frac{2}{16}$	$\frac{3}{16}$	$\frac{4}{16}$	$\frac{3}{16}$	$\frac{2}{16}$	$\frac{1}{16}$

The probability that Tina will get a sum of 6 with two spins is $P(\text{sum of } 6) = \frac{3}{16}$. To calculate the probability that Tina will not get a sum of 6, find the sum of the probabilities of the other outcomes.

$$P(\text{sum not } 6) = \frac{1}{16} + \frac{2}{16} + \frac{3}{16} + \frac{4}{16} + \frac{2}{16} + \frac{1}{16}$$

$$= \frac{13}{16}$$

The probability that Tina will not get a sum of 6 is $\frac{13}{16}$. The event that Tina gets a sum of 6 and the event that Tina does not get a sum of 6 are complementary events.

17.3 Calculating Compound Probabilities

A compound event combines two or more events using the word "and" or the word "or."

Example

Raul flips a coin and randomly draws a card from the stack of letter cards shown. He wants to determine the probability of flipping heads and drawing a vowel. He also wants to determine the probability of flipping heads or drawing a vowel.

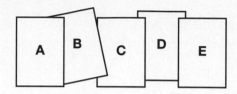

The ten possible outcomes are displayed in the tree diagram.

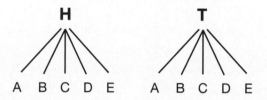

There are five outcomes that involve flipping heads, but only two of those outcomes involve drawing a vowel. Therefore, the probability of flipping heads *and* drawing a vowel is:

$$P(\text{heads and vowel}) = \frac{2}{10} \text{ or } \frac{1}{5}$$

To determine the probability of flipping heads *or* drawing a vowel, it is best to list the possible outcomes of each event. The possible outcomes for flipping heads is (H, A), (H, B), (H, C), (H, D), and (H, E). The possible outcomes for drawing a vowel is (H, A), (H, E), (T, A), and (T, E). There are a total of nine outcomes listed for the two events, but the outcomes (H, A) and (H, E) are listed in both events. Therefore, there are only seven outcomes that involve flipping heads or drawing a vowel. So, the probability of flipping heads or drawing a vowel is:

$$P(\text{heads and vowel}) = \frac{7}{10}$$

Using Simulations to Estimate Compound Probabilities

Many events involve very advanced rules for probability. In most cases, a simulation can be used to model the event.

Example

The table displays the probability that Kara will knock down each number of pins with the first ball thrown in any frame.

Number of Pins	10	9	8	7	6	5	4	3	2	1	0
Percentage of Attempts	65%	12%	8%	5%	3%	2%	1%	1%	1%	1%	1%

A simulation can be used to determine the experimental probability that Kara will throw three consecutive strikes. A random number generator is used to generate a random number from 00 to 99. The numbers from 00 to 64 are assigned to a strike. One trial consists of choosing 3 random two-digit numbers and counting how many of the two-digit numbers are from 00 to 64. The results of 20 trials are displayed in the table.

Trial Number	Count of Numbers 00 through 64	Trial Number	Count of Numbers 00 through 64
1	2	11	3
2	3	12	2
3	2	13	1
4	1	14	2
5	3	15	2
6	2	16	1
7	0	17	3
8	2	18	1
9	1	19	2
10	2	20	3

In 5 of the 20 trials, the simulation resulted in three strikes. Therefore, the experimental probability that Kara will make three consecutive strikes is:

$$P(3 \text{ strikes}) = \frac{5}{10} \text{ or } 0.25$$

The actual theoretical probability is ~0.27.

17

17

GLOSSARY

acute angle

An acute angle is an angle whose measure is greater than 0° but less than 90°.

Examples

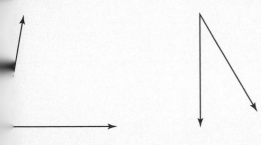

additive inverses

Two numbers with the sum of zero are called additive inverses. An Identity Property that states for every rational number a, $a + (-a) = 0$ designates the opposite of a number as the additive inverse.

Example

$6 + (-6) = 0 \quad -0.45 + 0.45 = 0 \quad \frac{3}{13} + \frac{-3}{13} = 0$

adjacent angles

Adjacent angles are two angles that share a common vertex and a common side.

Examples

Angles BAC and CAD are adjacent angles. The angles share the vertex A and the side AC.

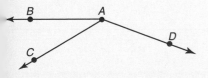

algebraic expression

An algebraic expression, sometimes shortened to be called an expression, is a mathematical phrase involving at least one variable and sometimes numbers and operation symbols.

Examples

$a \quad 2a + b \quad xy \quad \frac{4}{p}$

$z^2 \quad \sqrt{(4y + 4)^2} \quad 2.5 \times 10^y$

angle

An angle is formed by two rays that share a common endpoint.

Example

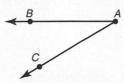

Angle BAC is formed by the rays $\overrightarrow{AB}$ and $\overrightarrow{AC}$ with a common endpoint at A.

angle bisector

If a ray is drawn through the vertex of an angle and divides that angle into two angles of equal measure, or two congruent angles, then the ray is called an angle bisector.

Example

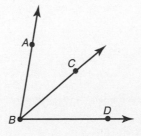

Ray BC is an angle bisector. It bisects angle ABD to create two congruent angles: angles ABC and CBD.

Glossary

arc

An arc is a part of a circle. It is the curve between two points on a circle.

Example

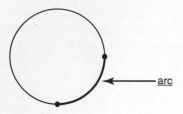

aspect ratio

An aspect ratio of an image is the ratio of its width to its height. Aspect ratios are written as two numbers separated by a colon (width : height).

Example

Aspect ratios are used to determine the screen sizes for movie screens and televisions.

B

bar notation

Bar notation is used for repeating decimals. A bar is drawn over digits that repeat.

Example

$\frac{2}{3} = 0.66666666\ldots = 0.\overline{6}$

---

base of a pyramid

The base of a pyramid is a single polygonal face. Similar to prisms, pyramids are classified by their bases.

Example

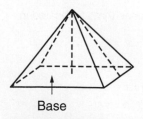

Base

---

bisect

To bisect means to divide into two equal parts.

C

census

A census is the collection of data from every member a population.

Example

The U.S. <u>Census</u> is taken every 10 years. The U.S. government counts every member of the population every 10 years.

---

center of a circle

The center of a circle is the point from which all points on the circle are equidistant. Circles are named by the center point.

---

circle

A circle is a collection of points on the same plane equidistant from the same point.

---

coefficient

A coefficient is the number that is multiplied by a variable in an algebraic expression.

Examples

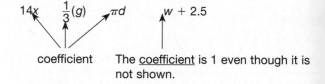

$14x \qquad \frac{1}{3}(g) \qquad \pi d \qquad w + 2.5$

coefficient   The <u>coefficient</u> is 1 even though it is not shown.

---

combining like terms

When you simplify expressions by adding or subtracting like terms, you are combining like terms.

Example

$4x + 3p + x + 2 = 5x + 3p + 2$
$24a^2 + 2a - 9a^2 = 15a^2 + 2a$

---

commission

A commission is an amount of money a salesperson earns after selling a product.

Example

5% commission on \$350
$.05 \times 350 = \$17.50 \leftarrow$ commission

Glossary

common factor

A common factor is a number or an algebraic expression that is a factor of two or more numbers of algebraic expressions.

Example

5(12) + 5(9) = 5(12 + 9)

5 is a common factor of both 5(12) and 5(9).

compass

A compass is a tool that is used to create arcs and circles.

complementary angles

Two angles are complementary angles if the sum of their angle measures is equal to 90°.

Example

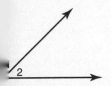

∠1 and ∠2 are complementary angles.

complementary events

Complementary events are events that consist of the desired outcome, and the remaining events that consist of all the undesired outcomes.

compound event

A compound event combines two or more events, using the word "and" or the word "or."

congruent

Congruent means to have the same size, shape, and measure.

congruent angles

Congruent angles are two or more angles that have equal measures.

congruent geometric figures

Congruent geometric figures are figures that have exactly the same size and shape. This means that each part of one figure is congruent to each corresponding part of the other figure.

congruent line segments

Line segments that have the same length are called congruent line segments.

constant of proportionality

In a proportional relationship, the ratio between two values is always the same, or constant. This is called the constant of proportionality. You can typically use the variable k to represent the constant of proportionality.

construct

When you construct a geometric figure, you create it using only a compass and a straightedge.

convert

To convert a measurement means to change it to an equivalent measurement in different units.

Example

To convert 36 inches to feet, you can multiply:

$$36 \text{ in.} \left(\frac{1 \text{ ft}}{12 \text{ in.}} \right) = \frac{36 \text{ ft}}{12}$$
$$= 3 \text{ ft}$$

coplanar lines

Coplanar lines are two or more lines that are located in the same plane.

corresponding angles

Corresponding angles are angles that have the same relative positions in geometric figures.

Examples

Corresponding angles of the two quadrilaterals are listed below.

Angle *M* and angle *C* are corresponding angles.

Angle *A* and angle *O* are corresponding angles.

Angle *T* and angle *I* are corresponding angles.

Angle *H* and angle *N* are corresponding angles.

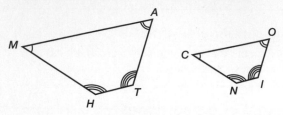

corresponding sides

Corresponding sides are sides that have the same relative positions in geometric figures.

Example

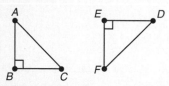

Sides *AB* and *DE* are <u>corresponding sides</u>.

cross-section

A cross-section of a solid is the two-dimensional figure formed by the intersection of a plane and a solid when a plane passes through the solid.

Example

The cross section of the cylinder is a circle.

data

When information is collected, the facts or numbers gathered are called data.

Examples

Heights of different animals at the zoo, area covered b different U.S. cities in square miles.

degrees

One unit of measure of angles is degrees (°).

depreciation

Depreciation is the decline in value of an item over time.

Example

The value of a car usually depreciates, or decreases in value, over time.

diameter

The diameter of a circle is the distance across the circl through the center. The diameter is equal to twice the radius of the circle.

Example

In circle *O*, segment *AB* is a diameter. The diameter *AB* is equal to twice the radius *OA*. The radius *OA* is 6 centimeters, so the diameter *AB* is 12 centimeters.

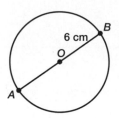

direct proportion

When two variables, *y* and *x*, are related in such a way that $y = kx$ with *k* being the constant of proportionality, the variables form a direct proportion. You can say that *y* is directly proportional to *x*.

Glossary

rect variation

A function represents a direct variation if the ratio between the output values and input values is a constant. The quantities are said to vary directly.

Example

If Melissa earns $8.25 per hour, then the amount she earns is in direct variation with the number of hours she works. The amount $8.25 is the constant of proportionality.

Distributive Property of Division over Addition

The Distributive Property of Division over Addition states that if a, b, and c are real numbers and $c \neq 0$, then $\frac{a + b}{c} = \frac{a}{c} + \frac{b}{c}$.

Examples

$$\underbrace{\frac{1 + 2}{4}}_{\frac{3}{4}} = \underbrace{\frac{1}{4} + \frac{2}{4}}_{\frac{3}{4}}$$

$$\underbrace{\frac{3}{16} + \frac{9}{16}}_{\frac{12}{16} = \frac{3}{4}} = \underbrace{\frac{3 + 9}{16}}_{\frac{12}{16} = \frac{3}{4}}$$

Distributive Property of Division over Subtraction

The Distributive Property of Division over Subtraction states that if a, b, and c are real numbers and $c \neq 0$, then $\frac{a - b}{c} = \frac{a}{c} - \frac{b}{c}$.

Examples

$$\underbrace{\frac{6 - 3}{5}}_{\frac{3}{5}} = \underbrace{\frac{6}{5} - \frac{3}{5}}_{\frac{3}{5}}$$

$$\underbrace{\frac{4}{12} - \frac{3}{12}}_{\frac{1}{12}} = \underbrace{\frac{4 - 3}{12}}_{\frac{1}{12}}$$

Distributive Property of Multiplication over Addition

The Distributive Property of Multiplication over Addition states that for any real numbers a, b, and c, $a \cdot (b + c) = a \cdot b + a \cdot c$

Examples

$$2(13 + 5) = 2(13) + 2(5)$$
$$2(18) = 26 + 10$$
$$36 = 36$$

$$\frac{1}{4} \cdot (8 + 4) = (\frac{1}{4} \cdot 8) + (\frac{1}{4} \cdot 4)$$
$$\frac{1}{4} \cdot 12 = \frac{8}{4} + \frac{4}{4}$$
$$\frac{12}{4} = \frac{12}{4}$$

Distributive Property of Multiplication over Subtraction

The Distributive Property of Multiplication over Subtraction states that if a, b, and c are any real numbers, then $a \cdot (b - c) = a \cdot b - a \cdot c$.

Examples

$$2(13 - 5) = 2(13) - 2(5)$$
$$2(8) = 26 - 10$$
$$16 = 16$$

$$\frac{1}{4} \cdot (8 - 4) = (\frac{1}{4} \cdot 8) - (\frac{1}{4} \cdot 4)$$
$$\frac{1}{4} \cdot 4 = \frac{8}{4} - \frac{4}{4}$$
$$\frac{4}{4} = \frac{4}{4}$$

draw

When you draw a geometric figure, you create it using tools such as a ruler, a straightedge, a compass, or a protractor.

endpoints

The endpoints of a line segment are the points where the line segment begins and ends.

Example

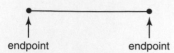

endpoint   endpoint

equally likely

When the probabilities of all the outcomes of an experiment are equal, then the probabilities are called equally likely.

equation

An equation is a mathematical sentence that is created by placing an equals sign, =, between two expressions.

Examples

$y = 2x + 4$

$6 = 3 + 3$

$2(8) = 26 - 10$

$\frac{1}{4} \cdot 4 = \frac{8}{4} - \frac{4}{4}$

equivalent ratios

Equivalent ratios are ratios that represent the same part-to-part or the same part-to-whole relationship.

evaluate an algebraic expression

To evaluate an algebraic expression, replace each variable in the expression with a number or numerical expression and then perform all possible mathematical operations.

Example

Evaluate the expression $\frac{4x + (2^3 - y)}{p}$ for $x = 2.5$, $y = 8$, and $p = 2$.

• First replace the variables with numbers:

$$\frac{4(2.5) + (2^3 - 8)}{2}$$

• Then calculate the value of the expression:

$$\frac{10 + 0}{2} = \frac{10}{2} = 5$$

event

An event is one or a group of possible outcomes for a given situation.

experiment

An experiment is a situation involving chance that lead to results, or outcomes.

experimental probability

Experimental probability is the ratio of the number of times an event occurs to the total number of trials performed.

Exterior Angle Inequality Theorem

The Exterior Angle Inequality Theorem states that the measure of an exterior angle of a triangle is greater tha the measure of either of the remote interior angles of the triangle.

Exterior Angle Theorem

The Exterior Angle Theorem states that the measure of the exterior angle of a triangle is equal to the sum of the measures of the two remote interior angles of the triangle.

factoring

To factor an expression means to rewrite the expression as a product of factors.

Example

$5(12) + 5(9) = 5(12 + 9)$

geometric construction

When a figure is created using only a compass and a straightedge, it is called a geometric construction.

geometric figures

Geometric figures are figures composed of lines, line segments, points, lines, rays, angles, and arcs.

eatest common factor (GCF)

e greatest common factor (GCF) is the largest factor
t two or more number or terms have in common.

ample

$x + 35$
ce 7 is the greatest common factor of 14 and 35 this
pression can be written as
$2x + 5)$

―――――― **H** ――――――

eight of a pyramid

e height of a pyramid is the perpendicular distance from
e vertex of the pyramid to the base of the pyramid.

ample

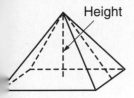

Height

―――――― **I** ――――――

ncluded angle

n included angle is the angle whose sides are made
p of the specific sides of the triangle.

xample

n triangle *ABC*, angle *A* is the included angle formed by
onsecutive sides $\overline{AB}$ and $\overline{AC}$.

A

C   B

ncluded side

An included side is a side between the two specific
angles of the triangle.

Example

n triangle *ABC*, $\overline{AB}$ is the included side formed by
consecutive angles *A* and *B*.

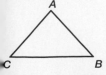

A

C   B

inscribed circle

An inscribed circle is a circle that fits exactly within the
boundaries of another shape. It is the largest possible
circle that will fit inside a plane figure.

Example

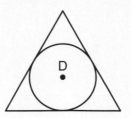

D

interest

When you save money in a bank savings account, the
bank pays you money each year and adds it to your
account. This additional money is interest.

intersection

An intersection is the point at which two or more lines
or arcs intersect, or cross.

Example

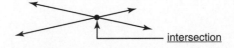

intersection

inverse operations

Inverse operations are operations that undo each other.

Examples

Addition and subtraction are inverse
operations: $351 + 25 - 25 = 351$.

Multiplication and division are inverse operations:
$351 \times 25 \div 25 = 351$.

―――――― **L** ――――――

lateral edges of a pyramid

The lateral edges of a pyramid are the edges formed by
the intersection of two lateral faces.

Example

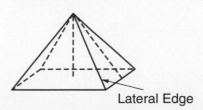

Lateral Edge

lateral faces of a pyramid

The lateral faces of a pyramid are the triangular faces of the pyramid. All lateral faces of a pyramid intersect at a common point.

Example

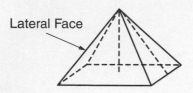

Lateral Face

like terms

Terms whose variable portions are the same are called like terms.

Examples

like terms

$$4x + 3p + x + 2 = 5x + 3p + 2$$

like terms

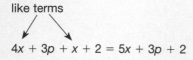

$$24a^2 + 2a - 9a^2 = 15a^2 + 2a$$

no like terms

$$m + m^2 - x + x^3$$

line

A line is described as a straight, continuous arrangement of an infinite number of points.

line segment

A line segment is a portion of a line that includes two points and all the points between those two points.

Example

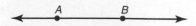

$\overline{AB}$ is a line segment.

linear pair

A linear pair of angles are two adjacent angles that ha noncommon sides that form a line.

Example

Angles 1 and 2 are a linear pair.

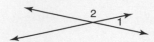

mean absolute deviation

The mean absolute deviation is the average of the absolute values of the deviations of each data value from the mean.

means and extremes method

The means and extremes method involves solving a proportion by setting the product of the means equal to the product of the extremes and then solving the resulting equation to find the unknown quantity.

Example

$$\frac{1}{2} = \frac{x}{9}$$
$$9 \times 1 = 2x$$
$$\frac{9}{2} = x$$
$$4.5 = x$$

midpoint of a segment

The midpoint of a segment is a point that divides the segment into two congruent segments, or two segments of equal length.

Example

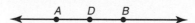

Point D is the midpoint of line segment AB.

multiplicative inverse

Multiplicative inverses are two numbers that when multiplied together equal 1.

Examples

The multiplicative inverse of $\frac{3}{7}$ is $\frac{7}{3}$:
$$\frac{3}{7} \times \frac{7}{3} = \frac{21}{21} = 1.$$

The multiplicative inverse of 5 is $\frac{1}{5}$:
$$\frac{5}{1} \times \frac{1}{5} = \frac{5}{5} = 1.$$

Glossary

multiplying by the reciprocal

When you multiply a term with a fractional coefficient by the multiplicative inverse of the fraction, you can isolate the variable on one side of the equation. This is known as multiplying by the reciprocal. When you multiply any number by its reciprocal, the result is 1.

Example

$0 = \frac{1}{2}x$ multiplying by the reciprocal

$\downarrow$

$(10) = \frac{2}{1}(\frac{1}{2}x)$

$20 = 1x$

—— N ——

non-repeating decimal

A non-repeating decimal neither terminates nor repeats.

Examples

$\sqrt{2} = 1.414213562373095\ldots$
$\sqrt{29} = 5.385164807134504\ldots$

---

non-terminating decimal

A non-terminating decimal is a decimal that continues without end.

Examples

$\sqrt{2} = 1.414\ldots$ $\sqrt{29} = 5.385\ldots$
$\frac{2}{3} = 0.6666666\ldots$

---

non-uniform probability model

When all probabilities in a probability model are not equivalent to each other, it is called a non-uniform probability model.

—— O ——

obtuse angle

An obtuse angle is an angle whose measure is greater than 90° but less than 180°.

Example

origin

The origin is the point on a graph with ordered pair (0, 0).

Example

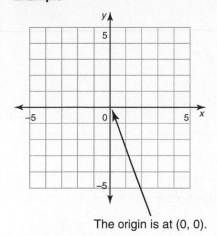

The origin is at (0, 0).

---

outcome

An outcome is the result of a single trial of an experiment.

—— P ——

parameter

When data are gathered from a population, the characteristic used to describe the population is called a parameter.

Example

If you wanted to find out the average height of the students at your school, and you measured every student at the school, the characteristic "average height" would be a <u>parameter</u>.

---

percent decrease

A percent decrease occurs when the new amount is less than the original amount. It is a ratio of the amount of decrease to the original amount.

Example

The price of a $12 shirt has decreased to $8.
$$\frac{\$12 - \$8}{\$12} = \frac{\$4}{\$12} = 0.\overline{3} = 33.\overline{3}\%$$
The <u>percent decrease</u> is $33.\overline{3}\%$.

Glossary

percent equation

A percent equation is written in the form percent × whole = part, where the percent is often written as a decimal.

Example

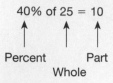

40% of 25 = 10

Percent   Part
      Whole

percent increase

A percent increase occurs when the new amount is greater than the original amount. It is a ratio of the amount of increase to the original amount.

Example

The price of a $12 shirt has increased to $13.20.

$$\frac{\$13.20 - \$12}{\$12} = \frac{\$1.20}{\$12} = 0.1 = 10\%$$

The <u>percent increase</u> is 10%

perpendicular

Two lines, line segments, or rays are perpendicular if they intersect to form 90° angles. The perpendicular symbol is ⊥.

Example

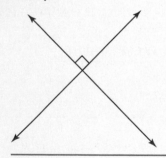

perpendicular bisector

A perpendicular bisector is a line, line segment, or ray that intersects the midpoint of a line segment at a 90° angle.

Example

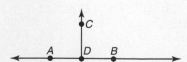

Ray *DC* is a <u>perpendicular bisector</u> of line segment *AB*.

pi (π)

The number pi is the ratio of the circumference of a circle to its diameter. That is,

$$pi = \frac{circumference\ of\ a\ circle}{diameter\ of\ a\ circle}.$$

plane

A plane is described as a flat surface. A plane has infinite length and width but no depth.

point

A point is described as a location in space.

population

The population is the entire set of items from which data can be selected. When you decide what you want to study, the population is the set of all elements in which you are interested. The elements of that population can be people or objects.

Example

If you wanted to find out the average height of the students at your school, the number of students at the school would be the <u>population</u>.

probability

Probability is a measure of the likelihood that an event will occur.

principal

The original amount of money originally invested is the principal.

probability model

A probability model is a list of each possible outcome along with its probability.

Properties of Equality

The Properties of Equality allow you to balance and solve equations involving any number. These properties include the Addition Property of Equality, the Subtraction Property of Equality, the Multiplication Property of Equality, and the Division Property of Equality.

Examples

Addition Property of Equality:
  If $a = b$, then $a + c = b + c$.

Subtraction Property of Equality:
  If $a = b$, then $a - c = b - c$.

Multiplication Property of Equality:
  If $a = b$, then $a \times c = b \times c$.

Division Property of Equality:
  If $a = b$, and $c \neq 0$, then $\frac{a}{c} = \frac{b}{c}$.

proportion

A proportion is an equation that states that two ratios are equal.

Example

$\frac{}{} = \frac{4.5}{9}$

protractor

A protractor is a tool that can be used to approximate the measure of an angle.

pyramid

A pyramid is a polyhedron formed by connecting one polygonal face to several triangular faces.

Example

A pyramid is named according to the shape of its base. The pyramid below is a triangular pyramid.

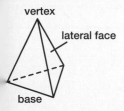

vertex
lateral face
base

radius

The radius is the distance from the center of a circle to a point on the circle.

Example

In the circle, O is the center and the length of segment OA is the radius.

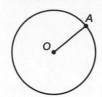

random number generator

A random number generator is any computer program or calculator that can generate numbers such that each number has an equal chance of occurring each time.

Example

You can use a graphing calculator and follow steps to generate random numbers.

random number tables

Random number tables are tables that display random numbers. These tables can contain hundreds of digits.

Example

Line 7	54621	62117	55516	40467
	11268	80811	14821	74154
	83479	55516		

random sample

A random sample is a sample that is selected from the population in such a way that every member of the population has the same chance of being selected.

Example

If you wanted to find out the average height of the students at your school, you could choose just a certain number of students randomly and measure their heights. This group of students would be a <u>random sample</u>.

range

The range of the data refers to the minimum and maximum values in a data set.

rate

A rate is a ratio that compares two quantities that are measured in different units.

Example

The speed of 60 miles in two hours is a <u>rate</u>:
$\frac{60 \text{ mi}}{2 \text{ h}} = \frac{30 \text{ mi}}{1 \text{ h}}$.

ratio

A ratio is a comparison of two quantities that uses division.

Example

The <u>ratio</u> of stars to circles is $\frac{3}{2}$, or 3:2, or 3 to 2.

The <u>ratio</u> of circles to stars is $\frac{2}{3}$, or 2:3, or 2 to 3.

ray

A ray is a portion of a line that begins at a point and extends infinitely in one direction. Rays are named using two points. The first point represents the starting point, and the second point can be any other point on the ray.

Examples

There are five rays labeled: ray *DA*, ray *BA*, ray *BD*, ray *DB*, and ray *AB*.

regular pyramid

A regular pyramid is a pyramid in which the base is a regular polygon.

remote interior angle of a triangle

The remote interior angles of a triangle are the two angles that are not adjacent to the specified exterior angle.

Example

The remote interior angles with respect to exterior angle 4 are angles 1 and 2.

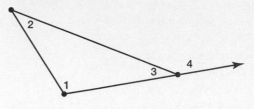

repeating decimal

A repeating decimal is a decimal in which a digit or a group of digits repeats without end.

Examples

$\frac{1}{9} = 0.\overline{1}$ $\frac{2}{9} = 0.\overline{2}$ $\frac{3}{9} = 0.\overline{3}$

repeating decimals

right angle

A right angle is an angle whose measure is equal to 90°. A square drawn at the vertex of the angle is used to indicate a right angle in geometric figures.

Example

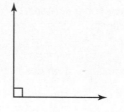

—————— S ——————

sample

When data are collected from a part of the population, the data are called a sample.

Example

If you wanted to find out the average height of the students in your school, you could choose just a certain number of students and measure their heights. The heights of the students in this group would be your <u>sample</u>.

sample size

When selecting a random sample, the number of members of the population selected to be in the sample is called the sample size.

sample

If you wanted to find out the average height of the students in your school, you could choose just a certain number of students randomly and measure their heights. The number of students in this group would be your <u>sample size</u>.

sample space

A list of all possible outcomes of an experiment is called a sample space.

scale drawings

Scale drawings are representations of real objects or places that are in proportion to the objects or places they represent.

Example

Maps and blueprints are examples of <u>scale drawings</u>.

scale factor

The ratio of side lengths in the scaled figure to those of the original figure is called the scale factor.

Example

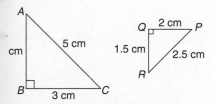

The <u>scale factor</u> from triangle *ABC* to triangle *PQR* is $\frac{1}{2}$.

scaling down

Scaling down means you divide the numerator and denominator by the same factor.

Example

scaling up

Scaling up means you multiply the numerator and denominator by the same factor.

Example

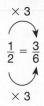

segment bisector

A segment bisector is a line, line segment, or ray that divides a line segment into two line segments of equal measure, or two congruent line segments.

Example

Ray *CD* is a <u>segment bisector</u>. It bisects line segment *AB*.

sides of an angle

The sides of an angle are the two rays that form the angle.

simple event

A simple event is an event consisting of one outcome.

simple interest

Simple interest is a fixed percentage of the principal. Simple interest is paid over a specific period of time—twice a year or once a year, for example.

simulation

A simulation is an experiment that models a real-life situation.

sketch

When you sketch a geometric figure, you create it without the use of tools.

skew lines

Skew lines, or non-coplanar lines, are lines that are not located in the same plane.

Example

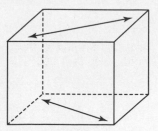

slant height of a pyramid

The slant height of a regular pyramid is the altitude of the lateral faces.

Example

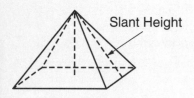

Slant Height

solve a proportion

To solve a proportion means to determine all the values of the variables that make the proportion true.

solve an equation

When you set expressions equivalent to each other and identify which value or values could replace the variable to make the equation true, you are solving an equation.

spread

The spread of data describes how "spread out" the data is. This can also be called the variability of the data.

spreadsheet

A spreadsheet is a computer document that allows you to organize information in rows and columns. Computer spreadsheets typically have a number of tools such as mathematical formulas and functions that make it easy to analyze information.

statistic

When data are gathered from a sample, the characteristic used to describe the sample is called a statistic.

Example

If you wanted to find out the average height of the students in your school, and you chose just a certain number of students randomly and measured their heights, the characteristic "average height" would be called a statistic.

straight angle

A straight angle is an angle whose measure is equal to 180°.

Example

$\angle ADB$ is a straight angle.

straightedge

A straightedge is a ruler with no numbers.

supplementary angles

Two angles are supplementary angles if the sum of their angle measures is equal to 180°.

Example

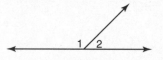

$\angle 1$ and $\angle 2$ are supplementary angles.

surface area

The surface area of a solid three-dimensional object is the total area of the outside surfaces of the solid. Surface area is described using square units of measure.

survey

A survey is one method of collecting information about a certain group of people. It involves asking a question or set of questions of those people.

Example

A restaurant may ask its customers to complete a survey with the following questions:

On a scale of 1–10, with 1 meaning "poor" and 10 meaning "excellent," how would you rate the food you ate?

□ 1 □ 2 □ 3 □ 4 □ 5 □ 6 □ 7 □ 8 □ 9 □ 10

On a scale of 1–10, with 1 meaning "poor" and 10 meaning "excellent," how would you rate the friendliness of your server?

□ 1 □ 2 □ 3 □ 4 □ 5 □ 6 □ 7 □ 8 □ 9 □ 10

— T —

terminating decimal

A terminating decimal has a finite number of digits, meaning that the decimal will end, or terminate.

Example

0.9 ←——— terminating decimal
)2.7

theoretical probability

Theoretical probability is the mathematical calculation that an event will happen in theory.

tree diagram

A tree diagram is a tree-shaped diagram that illustrates sequentially the possible outcomes of a given situation.

Example

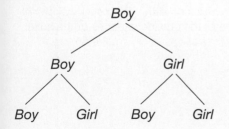

trial

Each time you repeat an experiment, it is called a trial.

Triangle Inequality Theorem

The Triangle Inequality Theorem states that the sum of the lengths of any two sides of a triangle is greater than the length of the third side.

Triangle Sum Theorem

The Triangle Sum Theorem states that the sum of the measures of the interior angles of a triangle is 180°.

two-step equation

A two-step equation requires that two inverse operations be performed in order to isolate the variable.

— U —

uniform probability model

A uniform probability model occurs when all the probabilities in a probability model are equally likely to occur.

unit rate

A unit rate is a comparison of two measurements in which the denominator has a value of one unit.

Example

The speed 60 miles in 2 hours can be written as a unit rate:

$$\frac{60 \text{ mi}}{2 \text{ h}} = \frac{30 \text{ mi}}{1 \text{ h}}.$$

The unit rate is $\frac{30 \text{ mi}}{1 \text{ h}}$, or 30 miles per hour.

unit rate of change

The unit rate of change is the amount the dependent value changes for every unit the independent value changes.

— V —

variability

The variability of data describes how spread out or clustered the data are in a data set.

Example

Range is one measure of the variability in a data set.

Glossary

variable

In algebra, a variable is a letter or symbol that is used to represent a quantity.

Examples

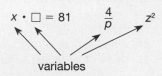

variables

vertex

The vertex of an angle is the common endpoint its two rays share.

Example

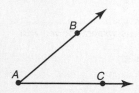

The <u>vertex</u> of angle *BAC* is point *A*.

vertex of a pyramid

The vertex of a pyramid is the point formed by the intersection of all lateral faces.

Example

Vertex

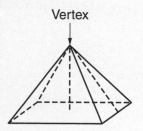

vertical angles

Vertical angles are two nonadjacent congruent angles that are formed by two intersecting lines.

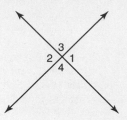

∠1 and ∠2 are <u>vertical angles</u>.
∠3 and ∠4 are <u>vertical angles</u>.

volume

The volume of a solid three-dimensional object is the amount of space contained inside the object. Volume is described using cubic units of measure.

――――― Z ―――――

zero pair

The integers -1 and $+1$ are a zero pair because their sum is 0.

Index

Index

Index

Index

Index • I-7